# BILY BROTHERS

## Wood Carvers and Clock Makers

# Books by Duane Hutchinson

*The Gunny Wolf and Other Fairy Tales*

*A Storyteller's Ghost Stories*

*A Storyteller's Ghost Stories, Book 2*

*A Storyteller's Ghost Stories, Book 3*

*Grotto Father, Artist-Priest of the West Bend Grotto*

*A Storyteller's Hometown*

*Storytelling Tips*

*Savidge Brothers, Sandhills Aviators*

*Exon, Biography of a Governor*

*Images of Mary*

*Doc Graham, Sandhills Doctor*

# Edited by Duane Hutchinson

*Franciscans Under Fire, Twenty Nuns, a Girl and a Dog*

# BILY BROTHERS

## Wood Carvers and Clock Makers

**Duane Hutchinson**

**Foundation Books**
Lincoln, Nebraska

Funded in part by a grant from the Iowa Arts Council.

**Library of Congress Cataloging-in-Publication Data**

Hutchinson, Duane.
    Bily brothers : wood carvers and clock makers / Duane Hutchinson.
-- 1st ed.
       p.   cm.
    Includes bibliographical references and index.
    ISBN 0-934988-30-7 (alk. paper) : $9.95
    1. Bily, Joseph, 1880-1964--Fiction. 2. Bily, Frank, 1884-1965-
-Fiction. 3. Clock and watch makers--Iowa--Spillville--Fiction.
4. Wood-carvers--Iowa--Spillville--Fiction. 5. Spillville (Iowa)-
-History--Fiction.  I. Title.
PS3558.U829B5   1993
813'.54--dc20                        93-11205
                                                CIP

First Edition
Most recent printing indicated by the first digit below.

1  2  3  4  5  6  7  8  9  10

The paper used in this publication meets the minimum requirements of American National Standard for Information Sciences - Permanence of Paper for Printed Library Materials, ANSI Z39.48-1984. ∞

*The words of my book nothing, the drift of it everything*
                                        --WALT  WHITMAN

# Contents

# Illustrations

*Between Pages 46 and 47*

1. Bust of Joseph Spillman [Speilmann], founder of Spillville, Iowa, from the Bily Brothers Statuary Clock.

2. Mary Bily and Anna Bily.

3. Bust of Antonin Dvořák from the Bily Brothers' Statuary Clock.

4. Charles Andera.

5. John Evangelist Bily.

6. Mary Bily, Frank Bily and Anna Bily preparing cabbage for sauerkraut.

7. Joseph Bily with horses.

8. Joseph Bily.

9. John Bily residence.

10. Bily carving of the Holy Family.

11. Anna Bily.

12. Joseph Bily with carpenter's square and plane.

Cover photo of Bily brothers is from the files of the *Telegraph Herald* newspaper in Dubuque, Iowa.

# Preface

How to tell the story of a quiet farm family who seldom went out in public, seldom visited with anyone beyond their few close neighbors, left few court records and left few newspaper accounts with the notable exception of their woodcarved clocks which brought the world to their door--that was the question.

At first it seemed this story of the Bily brothers should be a Czech story, because Bohemia cradled their parents and gave them the language they spoke in their Iowa farm home. Yet a look at their library and papers showed me they were enthusiastically American. They maintained an affectionate appreciation of Europe and its artistic and philosophical contributions, but their characteristic heroes included defenders of justice, artisans of beauty and inventors with genius and imagination. Native Americans and pioneer settlers appear frequently in the Bilys' carvings and often with a sense of the courage required of frontier life. Bohemia's own Antonin Dvořák appears more than twice, but so does George Washington.

Not until I constructed a timeline of their century, 1865-1964, did I see pattern and shape to their lives and art. The Bilys immigrated in the 1860s, took root in Iowa in the 1870s, and 1880s and along with other immigrants endured at a bare survival level. But always the future appeared bright. The birth of a "paralyzed child" in 1879, the first year of their marriage, may have tarnished that hope and may have contributed to Mary's shy reclusiveness. Her husband, John, persisted in winning and holding land, and worried when his sons, Joe and Frank, showed more interest in working with wood than with the soil.

During the Bilys' lifetime they went through identifiable clock carving periods. The scroll-saw fretwork clocks, for which they could order patterns, occupied their early years. The "Creation Clock," the "Capitol-Style Clock," the "Apostles Clock," the "Chimes of Normandy," the "Grand Tower" and the "Apostles' Parade Clock" represent classical patterns, some of which are still available from publishers such as Jim Reidle, Reidle Products, Box 58, Highway C, Yuba, Wisconsin 54634. As a youth, Jim Reidle, who is of Czech background, visited the Bilys with his father, a builder and carver of fretwork clocks. Jim shared with me an early 1900s catalog from H. L. Wild, Publisher, 279 East Tenth Street, New York City, an address I found several times among the Bily papers.

The Bilys' next period of clock making may be set off with a remark of Joe Bily. After he and Frank finished the massive "Apostles' Parade Clock," Joe reportedly said: "That's it! No more scroll-sawing!" They had hit a climax, a pinnacle of the scroll-saw fretwork. Frank would later say to a reporter, "That was our best; we didn't do any better."

But then Joe and Frank undertook an equally massive original work in the "American Pioneer History Clock." They returned to the bass relief-type carving that they had done at the beginning on the school desk. The "Plaque of the Holy Family" and the "Plaque of the First Thanksgiving" exemplify this period. Now they had Joseph's developed genius for design. Working from pictures found in school textbooks of American history, they first carved then built these carvings into a 500-pound piece of such unity and clarity of aesthetic vision, that it attracted the attention of national news organizations. *The Christian Science Monitor* applauded the Bilys' work. Henry Ford and his art advisors recognized the "American Pioneer History Clock" as worthy of financial investment and tried to buy it.

The publicity brought the tramp of strangers' feet through Mary Bily's parlor. The traffic plus the lack of room for display led the Bilys to acquire, or build, a farmyard display building. Mary's shy, reclusive daughter Anna did the unthinkable--she courageously met the lines of tourists and collected their dimes.

The "Statuary Clock," completed at the end of the 1920s, marks another turning point, the end of another era. The classic cabinet provided a way to gather up and display an accumulation of the busts of the Bilys' heroes. From dresser drawers and shop corners came the figures which represented Frank's carvings perhaps even from his school days.

Then, in the 1930s, came what might be called the Bilys' "Round and Leafy Period." If the observer stands back and looks at the "Struggle For Time Clock," the "Clock of the Forest," the "Elizabeth Fry Clock," the "Parade of Nations," the "Paradise" and the "On the Lookout" clocks, he sees a curving of lines, a roundness, often with leafy decorations. Perhaps it was the Bilys' love of the round-topped forests. The earlier cathedral-type clocks by contrast were pointed, gothic, and had sharply pointed spires pointing to the sky, where these later clocks have a softness of line.

Such are observations of the Bilys from the outside, but how did they feel inside? How did they interact? What were the topics of conversation over the kitchen table?

One incident of later years gives mute testimony to Anna's fear of poverty. When Robert Andera in the early winter of 1950 wired the Bilys' farmhouse "for the new owners, after the Bilys moved to Spillville," they found "the attic floor above the west bedroom . . . had one short board loose so it could be removed." Underneath they found "five one-pound tobacco cans. Four of the cans were about half full of coins with the top half stuffed with paper money. The fifth can was half full of coins and the top half stuffed with a 1929 newspaper. Frank and Joe said that Anna must have put it there because she was the only one that handled the money brought in from the showing of the clocks on display."[1]

---

[1] At the time the Rural Electrification Association, REA, was supplying power, Robert Andera, who had wired the Bilys' house, barn and clock display building in the mid-forties, came back to do additional wiring. Since considerable folklore has developed around this incident, I was happy to have Robert's written testimony. The quotations in this paragraph are from him. Robert Andera, Letter to Duane Hutchinson, 21 Jul. 1989, Author's collection.

Such an event gives insights into the Bilys' lives and relationships, not the least of which is the surprise and rapidity with which Anna's last illness must have overtaken her. She didn't have time or ability to tell about her private "bank" deposit under the floor of the attic.

The Bilys must have had many feelings about world events considering the reading they did. But obituaries don't tell that side of the story. Two reports in the newspapers give clues. One was that the Bilys had given up farming and rented out their land in the flourishing late 1920s, and then another news item in the early 1930s, at the depth of the Depression, indicated that Joe Bily had put in many hours grading roads with his horse-drawn road drag in order to work off his tax obligations. Had they turned over the farming to others too soon? Yet, the Bilys recovered whatever financial pressure they had endured and survived to sell their farm unencumbered.

My question grew in intensity--how to tell the story? For those private conversations which we will never recover, the feelings these artistic people must have experienced, it seemed to me, at last, that taking the diary form would be the best approach. This would be a way of revealing and not revealing. When the swirl of publicity and public attention surrounded them, Mary Bily may well have said little about it in her diary. That fame lay far down in her list of priorities. The diary became the place where she might confide her innermost thoughts, relations with her family and reflections on world events which she read about in Czech-language newspapers or heard mentioned by the Saint Wenceslaus priest.

My thanks go to the Iowa Arts Council who answered my application for partial funding with a grant.

My gratitude goes to Marlys Lien, librarian at South Winneshiek Schools, who suggested that as an artist-in-the-schools storyteller, I might want to look into the the story of the Bily Brothers at nearby Spillville. The same day Clark Goltz, then principal at "South Winn," took me over to Spillville to see the clocks. Marlys and Bob Lien followed me up with their support, offering me beautiful home hospitality on every one of my many working trips to Winneshiek County. Their contribution became a sort of "in kind matching grant." Their daughter Deb Rausch, though critically ill, gave me inspiration and encouragement in those early visits. I found myself wanting to do this story for her as well. Marlys even arranged a coffee for me in Spillville's Old World Inn and invited people of Spillville who might make unique contributions of oral history--Clarence Haug, Phyllis Riehle (who later gave my friends and me an historical walking tour of Spillville), Ray Kuboushek and others.

Notes on my desk from Marlys include mention of Stanley Maroushek of Decorah who had been a neighbor boy of the Bilys, had visited the Bilys many times, had enjoyed wood-carved toys they had made for him such as birds whose wings flapped, and who had inspired him with tips and tools on carving. In later years when a disabling illness ended his carpentry career, Stanley turned to woodcarving, turning out museum-quality pieces and teaching classes in wood carving.

Another note from Marlys suggested Donald Moore, DVM, who as a veterinarian had tested the Bilys' cattle. He enthusiastically led me to other sources, two of whom were Vernon and Thelma Brekke of West Union who had grown up as neighbors to the Bilys. Vernon's Grandpa Anderson had carved a "Chimes of Normandy Clock" from which the Bilys' got the idea to build theirs, and to put a music box in it. Vernon gave me the name of one of the Bilys' horses and much other detailed information

Helen Maroushek Bina of Calmar told me of going to the Brekke School, a one-roomed building a twenty minute hike south of the Bily's home, where Bilys attended a generation earlier. She spoke of "finding excuses to visit the Bilys." She was, she said, "the only little girl Anna Bily knew." And, in later years, said Helen, "when I invited Anna to my wedding, she came--a rare appearance in public--attired in old-fashioned dress-up clothing."

Of special delight and help have been Sister M. Raphael Bina and Sister Antonia Bina of the Notre Dame Convent, Omaha, Nebraska. They grew up in Spillville in the very house where Antonin Dvořák lived in the summer of 1893 and which later became the home of Bily Clocks. They told me of dancing to the player piano and of tending the garden out back. I saw one of them bend down and kiss a rose from a bush by the south foundation of Bily Clocks--a rose their dear mother had planted a half-century earlier. I stood with them

by the hour visiting in the late summer evening with Frank
Andera and other old friends. The exuberance of their faith
remains with me in the memory of their laughter and
kindness.

My thanks go also to Mark and Amy Balik who many
times talked to me in the Spillville Post Office, and where he
brought me specially made copies of photos he'd taken of the
Bily home in Czechoslovakia and told me the thrilling story
of finding the last living relative with the Bily name living
in the ancestral home.

My thanks to Mark's father, Bob Balik, longtime funeral
director of Spillville, as was his father. Bob answered many
of my questions, talked about his trips back to Czechoslovakia,
showed me his woodworking shop and spoke of "the Czech's
love for working in wood."

The Rev. Monsignor John Chihak graciously received me
in his home at Garner, Iowa, and helped me to know and
understand the Bilys better than I could have otherwise. He
was also able to give me insights on the Rev. Father Broz who
had also served the Bilys in times of sadness.

I am grateful for Mrs. Norman Poshusta, "Rusty" as she
is affectionately known, who has given uncounted thousands
of tours of Bily Clocks, trained dozens of young people to
interpret the clock museum and who never failed to respond to
me in my searchings, digging into files, speaking from her
comprehensive knowledge of the Bilys. Although she had
given the tour uncounted numbers of times, she still succeeded
in putting a new spark in tired tourists. I've seen people with
an "I've-seen-it-all look" as they came through the door pick
up with new excitement, gasp at amazing facts, laugh in the
funny places, and leave with a new spring in their steps. She
graciously received my son, Steve, when he came on a cold
day in December to spend several hours photographing the
clocks.

Joyce Fuchs also helped me in every way she could,
drawing on years of experience with Bily Clocks, always
patient and pleasantly thorough in answering my questions.

Thanks also to Mr. and Mrs. Richard Phillips of Fort
Atkinson, Iowa, for their seven-page handwritten letter
regarding the Bilys.

Ed and Linda Klimesh and all the staff of the Old World
Inn were most welcoming and served me many delicious

Czech meals. And some of the same young people who led tours of Bily Clocks switched over and served meals at lunch time. Later on a fun trip with my wife and granddaughters we spent an enjoyable overnight at the Old World Inn. I was grateful that Juanita Loven had filled me in on the story of the Inn's beginnings.

Mr. and Mrs. Tony Snyder of Ridgeway welcomed me into their home and spoke of their youth in the Bily neighborhood. Since he is a cabinet maker and finish carpenter he could give special insights on the Bilys' skills. He mentioned, for example, Joe Bily's mastering of the many intricacies of the carpenter's square more than seventy years ago, and of the Bilys' concern to teach the proper hammering of a nail so that a dent is never left in the wood.

Fritz and Marcella Kala received me into their home from the very first visit. There I got to meet their son, Bill. They told me of the early social customs of Spillville and of sawing ice out of the pond. They patiently tried to explain to me how a team of horses could pull an ice cutter through heavy ice and cut it into blocks. Fritz spoke of traveling from farm to farm butchering hogs and cattle, of making sausage, and of their delight in harvesting mushrooms spring and fall. Both Fritz and Marcella sang songs in Czech. They told me details of the Bily brothers coming to the tavern for the weekly supply of lager beer, and of Joe climbing up to wind the tavern clock. Fritz' brother George gave me more details of Spillville.

Becky Neuzil has been helpful with Czech costuming, hints on photography, and generally cheering me up. Frank Klimesh, gave me a good laugh when I needed it, and information whenever I asked. Clarence Haug explained the difference in the structure of Spillville's old north bridge and the south one which was later moved to a new location downriver. Joe Ryant led me to source people the night of the library meeting. Dale Goettelman told stories of the Bilys' life in Spillville, Iowa, in the home which he and Leanne have now owned and lived in for many years. They even opened their doors to our family.

My hearty thanks goes to Cyril Klimesh who has been a friend and a persistent source of help. He has answered every letter, fully, informatively and with enthusiasm for the

# BILY BROTHERS

project. His book has been a window into the pioneer history of this Czech immigrant community.[2]

John H. Marvin, of Madison, Wisconsin, has been a delightful correspondent. A specialist in Czech and Slovak geneology, he has helped many families find their roots overseas and has led many tours taking people "back home." I'm glad he took an interest in my questions.

Arlene Mashek, research assistant, and Paul Polansky with his new Czech Research Center in Spillville have dazzled me with computerized research into Czech geneology. He has answered questions with lightning speed and holds promise for much more help for American Czechs who want answers about their ancestors.

Thanks to Kim Glock and others at Winneshiek County offices.

I began by thanking a librarian friend, and I come to a close thinking of the help and encouragement given to me by many librarians: the staff of the reference department in the Bennett Martin Library, Lincoln City Libraries, Lincoln, Nebraska, the Nebraska State Historical Society Library, Lincoln, the State Historical Society Library at Iowa City, the Cedar Rapids Public Library, the Des Moines Public Library, the Decorah Public Library, the Winneshiek County Geneological Society, and especially Ruth Brooks of the Fayette County Geneological Society, West Union, Iowa.

I particularly appreciate the help of Duane Fenstermann, archivist of Luther College Library, Decorah, and Joyce Zoulek, Spillville Public Librarian, Saint Wenceslaus Church secretary and community worker.

Duane Fenstermann opened the way for me to search the microfilms of early day newspapers in Luther College's collection. He pointed me to information on the "ghost town" of Conover only three and a half miles southeast of the Bily farmstead along the Milwaukee and St. Paul Railway tracks, and why Conover first flourished, then fell. Duane also made a copy of the only known recording of Frank Bily's voice in an early radio interview

Joyce Zoulek helped me first and last, digging through her collections, showing me items she'd purchased on the Bily

---

[2]Cyril M. Klimesh, *They Came to This Place, A History of Spillville, Iowa and Its Czech Settlers* (Sebastopol, CA: Methodius Press, 1983).

sale including papers and a large framed print of Hradcaney Castle, Prague, Czechoslovakia, which had hung in the Bilys' home in the last years. And she made available to me a copy of *The Quasquicentennial History Book: 1860-1985, Spillville, Iowa,* which has been my constant companion since. She organized a Bily event to help me in my search for people with anecdotes about the Bilys and filled the library auditorium.

Katie Thompson, Recorder for Winneshiek County, Iowa, supplied me with her personal recollections of the Bily farm and Bily family vital statistics from the county record. Our thanks to Blanche Beall. She might be said to have been the Bilys' first publicist. Beall published stories in the *West Union Gazette* in the 1920s and in the late 1920s and early 1930s published and sold a series of editions of a booklet describing the Bily Clocks, a publication which evolved into the booklet sold in the Bily Clocks Museum.

Several newspapers also played an important part in this project. My thanks to them not only for recording part of the Bily story over the years but also for giving me permission to share some of their articles and photographs: John Anundsen of the Decorah Newspapers; Gary Sawyer, *Globe Gazette*; Brian Cooper, *Telegraph Herald*; Richard Fromm, *Decorah Republican.*

To others, not named above, my thanks. I wish I could name you all.

Last of all to Catherine Roberts who has read my manuscripts carefully and critically, Larry Shestak who inspected the manuscript for the appropriateness of Czech words and also sang Czech songs (*Sla Nanynka Do Zeli* and *Pisnicka Ceska Valcik*), Marlys Lien, Clark Goltz, my son Steve and my wife Marilyn Hutchinson who have carefully read my manuscript and made many suggestions and corrections--to you all my heartfelt thanks.

BILY BROTHERS

# Introduction

Death came early for Jan Andera,[3] at age twenty-two in Hrobska Zahradka, Bohemia. It had come early for his mother when he had reached only fourteen and she but thirty-seven. Jan left this world not knowing that someday thousands of people would drive across America to see his grandsons' wood carved clocks.

Jan left behind his beloved wife, Barbara, and a tiny baby girl, Marie, named after the mother of Jesus. If Jan had a dream of the future, he shared that dream with many other Czechs: "Land of our own!" With such a yearning, immigrants came from Czechoslovakia to the rolling hills and land along the wooded and picturesque Turkey River in northeast Iowa. Jan didn't get to see the Promised Land, but in 1862 his widow, Barbara, would accompany his father and stepmother to America, journeying with five-year-old Marie first to Toronto and then to Spillville, Iowa.,

In 1854 a small Czech community had formed at Spillville. On May 16, 1860, these new immigrants laid the cornerstone of Saint Wenceslaus church building on a hill above Spielmann's water-powered mill.

On September 28, 1860, Saint Wenceslaus Day, the gathered Czechs celebrated their first Mass with Father Henry

---

[3]Jan Andera died 12 Feb. 1857. Letter received from Cyril M. Klimesh, 26 April 1993.

**1**

Fedderman. The missionary priest came over from nearby
Festina, Iowa, near where the first Mass had been celebrated
in these lands west of the Mississippi.

In 1863, in a low farmhouse west of Spillville, Iowa,
Katerina Andera, 43, sat by her stepgrandchild, five-year-old
Marie. Katerina wore the traditional dress of Bohemian
farm women--not the bright colors of festivals, but the plain
grays of working people. She hung her homespun shawl on a
peg by the door.

Born in 1819 of the family Cekal in Bohemia, she spoke
with the rich sounds of the Czech language. Her mother,
Katerina Sakulinova Cekal, born in 1796 in the same
province, had taught her the language, the traditions of Saint
Wenceslaus and perhaps even the Bohemian fairy tales.

Now Grandma Andera and Marie worked awhile with the
stub of a pencil and scraps of paper, each drawing a portion of
a picture, then passing it to the other to finish. Grandpa
Frantisek Andera watched meditatively from a corner of the
room as he chewed on the stump of a pipe.

Then the two at the table began to write in a new leather-
covered book. The fresh cowhide smell of a bootshop floated in
the air. Grandma talked with Marie about what she wanted to
write. Then they worked earnestly at the book. Sometimes
both had their hands on the pencil as they guided the letters.
Each eagerly took the pencil in turn, made a few marks and
handed it back. Thus the diary began.

# 1.

# Mary's Youth

## *1865-1876*

**Sunday, January 1, 1865**

My grandma helps me write this. I always call her Grandma. My real grandma, Anna Balounova Andera, died before I came into this world.

Dear Diary, today I begin to write to you. I am Marie Andera. The American children call me Mary. My father, Jan Andera, died the year God gave me birth. He left this world at only twenty-two. My mother brought me, a five-year-old, to the New World along with Grandpa and Grandma Andera

I am seven years old. I pray to Holy Mary and Her Blessed Son that what I write here may be true. May I be true like Saint Wenceslaus. Thanks to my dear Grandma. She gave me this pretty leather book. She said I should write down all life. Someday I'll be happy I did.

This, my third year to live in the New World, makes me feel like an old-timer.

**Monday, January 2, 1865**
Dear Grandmother, you miss your Hrobska Zahradka home.[4]
I miss Bohemia too and I miss getting to know Papa. I wish he could have come with us to Iowa. Mother said he always used to say: "Someday we will own land in America."
I would like to see where President Abraham Lincoln lives. I'm afraid he will die with all the fighting. Why do all good people die, like Jesus and Saint Wenceslaus? I pray for courage to die for my Faith.

**Sunday, January 22, 1865**
Holy Mary. Pray for us sinners. I promised to write you every day, Dear Diary. The snow came. We went to Mass on the sled. The white fields push against the black forests. The snow made the hills look like mushroom shapes.
Grandmother says I like to make shapes. She gives me clay to mold sometimes. This winter she watched us make a fat-cheeked snowman with a bald head. We took extra snow like handfuls of plaster and bunched it around the edges of his head to make the ring of hair. Charles laughed when we finished.
Grandma says I'm a sculptor like my great-grandfather and my cousin Charles Andera.

**Sunday, January 29, 1865**
I left my shoes out and they got wet. When they dry out, I'll have to oil them extra.
Today we got a letter from our friends in Bohemia. They were the ones who said we shouldn't come through U.S.A. because of the war so we came through Canada.
One farmer in Iowa may own as much land as several farms in Bohemia.
Americans make houses out of logs like Abraham Lincoln's house. Others make Indian houses. They have dirt floors. Sometimes snakes come in. I wouldn't like that.

---

[4]Hrobska Zahradka means Cemetery Garden or Garden at the Graves. Letter received from Cyril M. Klimesh, 26 Apr. 1993.

**Sunday, February 5, 1865**

Dear Diary, you were put in the bottom of our trunk and I didn't know where you were. We still live out of our trunks. America has parades on the 4th of July for U.S.A.'s birthday. In Bohemia we had parades for Corpus Christi, only we called them processions. Here people march and carry the flag and give thanks for freedom. Saint Wenceslaus would like that, I think.

**February 1865**

Lent comes like a cloud of sadness.

Dear Diary, I seem to write to you only on Feast Days. Today we play before a long time of prayer and repentance. I put on my grandmother's white dress that she wore for her first communion.

We ate pickerel which the neighbors brought. The fish could stand almost as tall as I am if it could stand on its tail.

**Saturday, April 1, 1865**

They call this April Fool's Day and play tricks on each other. God plays tricks on me when I sleep. Sometimes I dream we are still on the boat. Then I say, "Please, God, don't let our family get sick on the boat." If one dies one gets put in the ocean. Then I wake up.

Dear Grandma, I love you and wish you could come to our house more often. You cried when you left your mother and father in the Old Country. Then you say, "We will all see each other again in heaven."

**Sunday, April 16, 1865**

Everybody in church today talked about President Lincoln. Why did he have to die? My tears wet the page. Father Mikota said Mr. Lincoln gave his life to save our United States.

**Monday, May 1, 1865**

Dear Diary, why do I dream the way I do? Sometimes I am on the other side of the world. I prayed that we wouldn't get sick on the boat. God didn't answer that prayer, but he gave us a better answer. He kept us alive. Some died.

Then the long trip on the train, and cinders in my clothes. There were brides going West, still dressed in their once-white wedding dresses.   I wonder if I will get married someday.

**Sunday, September 10, 1865**
Today my eighth birthday surprised me.   When Mama called me, I still dreamed.   I dreamed I walked, leaning on a cane, my hair white with age.   Then Mama called me again and I woke up.   Mama said that for my birthday I could sit anywhere I wanted to for my supper.   I chose to sit up on top of our trunk, just like I sat on the ship coming to America.   We had wild plum kolaches.
I think Grandma Andera likes to see me grow.

**Monday, October 9, 1865**
Today opens a new door for me.   I get to go to school at Martin Bouska's near the Turkey River.   It has a dirt floor and log seats.   Someday Saint Wenceslaus will have a school. The Poshustas will hitch up the team and drive me to school.

**Monday, September 17, 1865**
At school they told us about the 1,700 people who died when the steamship exploded on the Mississippi.   I thought we were all going to die on the ship crossing the Atlantic, but I didn't think of an explosion.

**Sunday, December 10, 1865**
Someday maybe we will have a log house.   But we will have a wood floor and no snakes.
And we have a stone church in Spielville, built before we came.[5]   The women and children helped carry the stones.   I wrote a letter to Bohemia about that.
I liked Father Spacek.   He drove his horse a long way to get here.   He taught us catechism and songs.   Now we have Father Urban.   He makes me think of an angry bear.   He frowns at us under his heavy eyebrows.

---

[5]The village of Spillville derived its name from the name of its founder, Joseph Spielman [Spielmann].   The community has also been known by the names Spielmansville, Speilville and Telford.   Klimesh, *They Came to This Place*, p. 76.

A couple of years ago a man a few miles from here shot a bear. We didn't think there were any left in the country. They should have kept him in a cage for the children to see.

**April 1866**
    They are building the railroad near Conover. Mr. Poshusta took his team of horses and helped them. He took us with his team and wagon over to see where they are building. A lot of other farmers were there to help with their horses.

**Tuesday, January 1, 1867**
    I don't write in my diary as often as I should. I'm sorry, Grandma. This year I will do better. But if I make my book last all my life like you said, I can only write a little each year. I will be ten years old this year. Ten times ten makes a hundred. I can't imagine living ten times this long. It has taken me forever to get this old. I wish I could speak English like some children I've heard. But we always speak Czech.

**Sunday, June 2, 1867**
    Father Mikota almost dances as he walks up the aisle. He smiles like an angel had lit a lamp inside his face. I like him. He doesn't have much hair on top. He makes me think of our bald snowman with a broad grin.
    Father Mikota talks to us about school. I would like to learn English, but no one here knows how to teach it.

**Thursday, July 15, 1867**
    Tonight I have a Daddy again. Mama laughs and hugs me. Then later she cried. I asked why she cried. Did she cry sad? She said, "I cry happy." Dear Papa Andera--I never got to know you. I hope you are smiling down from heaven.[6]

**Tuesday, September 10, 1867**
    Tonight we cut a layer cake for my tenth birthday. Grandma Andera came. The men cut corn and stood it up in

---

[6]July 15, 1867. Charles Poshusta married Barbara Cekal Andera, widow of Jan. His first wife, Anna Pribyl, died a young woman. Letter received from Cyril M. Klimesh, 28 Jul. 1990.

shocks. I like to crawl into the shocks and make a little house, like an Indian tipi I saw at the fort.[7]

**Saturday, February 29, 1868**
Grandma says that people born on this day may be old and white-haired and still only have twenty birthdays. She calls this Leap Day.
Papa said he feels sad the senators voted against President Johnson. Our schoolteacher said the Senate impeached Mr. Johnson because he tried to be fair to the South like Lincoln wanted. Mama says we are lucky to be in a country where people can vote even against the head of the government.

**Christmas Vacation, 1868**
It seems more like Christmas with a little baby in the house. My half brother Leopold came this year. He's my half brother, but he seems like a whole baby to me!
Mama taught me how to braid the vanocka.

**1869**
Now we have President Grant. Will he run our country like he ran his armies? Many of our families left Bohemia to get away from the army.

**1869**
A letter to the neighbors came from the Matej Bilys in New York. They came last year from Bohemia. The men have been working for the railroad in New York. They want to come to Iowa where there are people they know. Their thirteen-year-old son John already works on the railroad.

**1869**
Father Mikota rubs his palms in excitement over the new church additions. They are building wings and there'll be a balcony where the men's choir can sit. Father Mikota chuckles and grips his hands together as he walks around.

---

[7]The Flower Brothers Company, who in 1853 had invested an English widow's money in hundreds of acres of Fort Atkinson land, left in 1867, selling the land to a man named Bradley.

The women tell about carrying stones and mortar for the first construction. Now comes a bell tower with Mr. Spielmann's gift of brass bells. Some people say the church, when finished, will look like Saint Barbara's Church in Kutna, Hora, in Bohemia. But it would make my Grandma Cekal happy because she named my mother after Saint Barbara. But my cousin Charles says that's simply because of its cruciform--with the wings it will be like a cross if you looked down from the sky.

**1869**
Our new music professor from Bohemia gets us to sing like we've never sung before. Professor Kovarik also has a class for violin. When he plays sometimes it makes tears come to my eyes.

**Friday, September 10, 1869**
My twelfth birthday. Mama made special kolaches. If we were back in Bohemia, she would have made them from apples in the orchard there. These came from our neighbors.
Papa Poshusta said that in Roman times boys took the toga and became adults when they were twelve. I have to wait until I'm twenty-one in America. I think I could be a grown-up, but Mama doesn't.

**1870**
General Robert E. Lee died. Mama said he died of a broken heart. But I think he got too old. He had a white beard.

**1870**
Our church smells like fresh cement and varnish--almost finished now and we have a new school. Father Mikota gets people to do things they didn't think they could do.
And we can hear the church bells out in the country on still cold mornings. Papa Poshusta stopped to listen and pray when he heard the bells. Then he said, "And thank you, Mr. Spielmann." Mr. Spielmann gave the bells even though he's a German because he likes us.

**Sunday, December 25, 1870**
This year we have two babies to celebrate Christmas with us. Barbara giggles and spits bubbles when we light a candle.

Leopold walks around the tree we brought in from the pasture. He pulls at the branches carefully because he got pricked the first time. He tries to sing along when we sing Christmas hymns.

### Tuesday, October 10, 1871

Fire has raged in Chicago since Sunday. To think of a whole city devastated! Poor people who have lost loved ones and everything they owned! Papa Poshusta said people in Decorah talk about taking the train to see the burned-out city. Maybe they should just send the money the trip would have cost. That fire makes me careful to hang our lantern up on the hook in our barn.

### Tuesday, February 29, 1872

Here's that magic Leap Day! I told Leepy he has this day named for him. Girls can ask the boys to go with them, Grandma says. I would never do that, even if Leap Year tempts me.

### 1872

Newspapers tell how Germans ran the Jesuit priests out of the country.

### Sunday, May 26, 1872

If I could have a wish right now, it would be to go to New York and walk across the new Brooklyn Bridge. The picture in the paper makes it look like towers of toothpicks and threads. But if we had it over our Turkey River it could go clear across Spillville! Or, while I am asking my fairy godmother, I might ask to go to the new Yellowstone and watch Old Faithful geyser shoot up higher than our church.

### Monday, July 15, 1872

Today Mama and Papa Poshusta celebrate five years of marriage. I tried to explain to Leopold, Barbara and Wenzel that they just wouldn't be here if my mother hadn't married. Leepy said, "Would I still be in heaven?" I don't know. Do we come from heaven and go to heaven?

**Tuesday, September 10, 1872**
Today I became fifteen! One half of thirty. One fourth of sixty. Mama says I'm old enough to scrub a floor, or bake a cake, or milk a cow, but not old enough to get married.

**November 1872**
General Grant got re-elected. Papa Poshusta says, "President Grant looked the other way when he ran the government and the people looked the other way when they re-elected him." I wish people could be trusted, then President Grant wouldn't have troubles.

**Wednesday, September 10, 1873**
Dear Diary, you still look pretty in your leather cover after ten years. Grandma Andera must have saved her pennies to get you for me. I have heard that the grasshoppers not only eat crops but even eat the leather harnesses of the horses.
Sweet sixteen and never been kissed, they say. Well, I have been kissed, but I won't tell who. Somebody else might read this diary. Anyway, I'm not sweet--only when I want to be.
We got a letter from the Cekals back in Zahradka. It took three months to get here for my birthday. Hearing from Bohemia made up for a lot of what we read in the newspapers.

**Friday, September 4, 1874**
Today Grandma and Grandpa celebrate twenty-five years of marriage. Only they don't celebrate much. They're going to have a dinner though. And people will bring things in. I like that.

**Thursday, September 10, 1874**
My seventeenth! Sometimes I think about the things I would like to do when I'm a grown-up. Maybe some day the right man will come along. Then I suppose I'll help him with his work. But, sometimes I think I will go to New York and work for the Society for the Prevention of Cruelty to Children. Wouldn't that be more worthwhile than anything I could do here?
Father Mikota says we should be ready to say "Yes!" the way Mary did when the angel came to her. But I wonder if angels come anymore the way they used to. Maybe the angel

would come and look just like a farm boy and I wouldn't recognize him. Maybe he has already come and I said no! After all, Father Mikota said Mary was maybe only sixteen when the announcement came to her. I am already seventeen.

But none of the men I've met are angels. I'm sure of that.

They're putting the new clocks up in the church tower. Then we will be able to look up and see if we are late for Mass as we walk up the hill.

We are fortunate compared to some places where the grasshoppers have eaten all the crops.

**Wednesday, November 26, 1874**

We came back late tonight from Grandpa Frantisek's seventieth birthday party. He seemed to enjoy all the attention. He talked about his long life and how he and his son, Jan, had married sisters and about the nine-week voyage across the Atlantic.

**Friday, New Year's Day, 1875**

Today begins the diamond jubilee of this century. I stayed up reading a book until I heard the clock ding-dong midnight. How curious that in one second we leave a whole three-quarters of a century behind and can never ever get it back. One second present; one second past. Gone forever. I suppose Mama felt that way when Daddy died. Mama said, "One moment he looked at me; next moment his spirit had flown out the window." One second I had a Daddy; next second I became an orphan. I know I wasn't an orphan really because I had Mama. And now I have Papa Poshusta. But sometimes I think about Cinderella losing her mama and being an orphan.

**Tuesday, January 19, 1875**

Tonight my cousin Charles starts his new home with Barbara Dostal. I wonder if he carried her across the threshold? He's twenty-three and Barbara only eighteen--only a year older than me. He should be able to support them with his skills as a carpenter. He can carve wood so it looks like cut stone.

**Friday, September 10, 1875**
Today I am eighteen.

**Friday, December 31, 1875**
I write this late at night. The Diamond Jubilee Century Year flies away. As I listen to my memories of the year, I remember best the sounds of the new pipe organ filling the church.

**Tuesday, February 29, 1876**
Grandma Andera's Day--anyway I think of her on February 29th because she mentioned it. "God has given us an extra day, a Leap Day, to live," she said once.

**Tuesday, July 4, 1876**
Happy 100th birthday, America. I think of Benjamin Franklin and Saint Wenceslaus. Anyone else would laugh at the comparison. But each dared to face death for the liberty of his people. Franklin said, "If we don't hang together, we will hang separately." Saint Wenceslaus hung separately, so to speak. He didn't even have the support of his own brother. We are happy to be in America.

# 2.
# Marriage and Children
## *1878-1888*

**Tuesday, December 24, 1878**

Christmas Eve! Dear Diary, I have neglected you again, more than a year. And now, only a month remains until I marry John Bily. Much has happened. John's sister, Barbara, got us together. She had promised herself to John Poshusta. From those first days when Barbara and I took lunches out to the threshing crews, John paid me special attention. The four of us have walked together to hear Professor Kovarik's band. We have played Darde, holding up the cards to read them by firelight in the long winter evenings. Now we will stand at the altar together before our beloved Father Mikota.

**Monday, January 6, 1879**

John worked for the railroad and stayed in Calmar. He will buy a farm near Spillville if he can. If we save and put off getting the things we want, and if his father helps us, we can do it. Matej has said over and over, "I want my children

**15**

to have the land--land I never could have in the Old Country.
I came for my children. For me alone, I could have stayed in
Bohemia."

### Tuesday, January 21, 1879

Dear Diary, my wedding day--a day I suppose I have
looked forward to since a child and a day I have feared. Will
my husband die the way my father did and leave me alone?
Why should I think such thoughts on my day of happiness?

This morning the sun came up red in the east.

Oh, Dear Grandma Andera, I'm glad I feel I can share my
thoughts the way we used to. Your health has taken you from
us. You would have wisdom for me. You and I would talk
about things I wouldn't even talk to my own mother about. I
think you and John are a little alike. His kindness glows out
of him like heat from a stove. His eyes twinkle. I think he
will be a good father to our children.

### Sunday, March 2, 1879

I wonder if we will have children. I feel sad to see older
couples with no children. Abraham and Sarah in the Bible
seemed sad to me. We have plenty of time. Perhaps we will be
on our own farm. This room closes me in. Sometimes I want
to push the walls out. I cook on top of the heating stove.
Potatoes keep us alive. Now and then we have a penny-loaf of
bread. Going to Spillville on Sundays we fill up.

Tomorrow comes early for farmers who move from one
rented place to another and pack their furniture on hayracks
and wagons. Farm people agree on the first Monday in
March, to take up new places and plant new seed. Someday we
will be among them. The sky hangs heavy overhead as if it
could snow. When winter hangs on I'm sorry to see them
moving.

I wonder if the sun shines in Bohemia. I wonder if icicles
droop from thatched roofs? People don't move so much in
Bohemia. When they move they come to America.

John left early to go help a neighbor move out near
Spillville.

**Sunday, March 30, 1879**

During the night I felt hungry and ate part of a loaf of bread. Then this morning I lost my breakfast. It doesn't make sense, or does it?

**Sunday, April 13, 1879**

We may have our baby in our first year! Will people talk if the child comes early? We know we waited until marriage and that's all that matters.

The weather holds good. John wishes we had our land, but when storms roll overhead and roads lay in muddy ruts, I am glad to stay in Calmar. After the baby comes we can move.

**Sunday, June 29, 1879**

In June we celebrate Corpus Christi and July the birthday of U.S.A. For the Thursday Corpus Christi celebration the little girls wore flowers and frilly dresses their grandmothers had made, or had worn as children. I'm glad I had my grandma nearby, but we didn't wear frilly dresses when I grew up.

John hopes for a boy and mostly I do too. But at this time I'm wishing for a girl.

After Mass we walked down near Turkey River. The smell of summer blossoms came on the breeze. We have enjoyed the chokecherry, elderberry and plum. Bees buzzed round our ears. John's hands feel rough from mixing mortar.

Men in Spillville have work building Mr. Nockles' beer cellars.

This Friday we celebrate America's birthday. There will be speeches and a parade. Two parades within days, but so different, walking in procession with the Blessed Sacrament, or watching clowns, or watching the farmers with their dressed-up hay wagons. We will hear speeches about freedom.

**Sunday, September 28, 1879**

Saint Wenceslaus Feast Day.

Dear Diary, I seem to write you on feast days, those times I think of Grandmother Andera.

I am showing enough now that even women I do not know very well come up and ask me about the baby. I can feel the next generation moving within me. Who are you, little person? Will you grow up on a farm or live in this tiny room in town? Will you travel to a new world the way I did?

### Sunday, November 23, 1879

So many dark and dreary days this time of year! We are in the land of the Sun-horse and the light has gone away.[8] But John has work and we have hope for land in the future. Soon the baby will come and bring rays of sunshine into our home.

### Wednesday, December 24, 1879

Christmas Eve.

Dear Diary, there are three of us now with the coming of John Evangelist! Last Friday I thought for awhile that my dear husband would be left alone. The gates of heaven seemed close to me. You came, little Johnny, but terribly hurt. Oh, what will become of us?

But, we are alive. You are young; you will heal. Tonight, on Christmas Eve, the evening of the Child, Father Mikota held you up. Father held you up, little Johnny, after you received the water of baptism, and claimed you and named you for our Lord. Uncle Frank Bily, and Aunt Anna, stood with us.[9]

### Sunday, February 8, 1880

Dear Diary, my tears fill the night. Something goes wrong with my baby. And Father Mikota moved away. Where do we go for consolation?

A new pastor today--an old man, a stranger, stood at the altar. He can recite the history of the Hittites, and describe the road to Babylon, but will he get to know us?

### Sunday February 29, 1880

Leap Day! Blessed Mother, bless my child. A cold wind blows out of the north. New life of spring has not yet wakened. Rain runs down the window, splitting in two, then three,

---

[8]The Sun-Horse, a famous Bohemian fairy tale. Maurice Michael and Pamela Michael, "The Sun-Horse," *Fairy Tales from Bohemia* (Chicago: Follett Publishing Company, 1968) pp. 1-13.

[9]Despite the 1880 birth year on Jan's (John Evangelist Bily) grave there is evidence he was born December 19th of 1879.

making rivers that run on glass. Please heal little Johnny on this special God-gift Day!

### Sunday, March 28, 1880
Dear Diary, so soon again I feel the change. Only in December Johnny came. Hardly a year ago I wrote to you I could feel a child growing within me. Now I know another child comes. How I wanted everything to be right, but something has gone terribly wrong.
Oh, Grandmother, what can I do? Will it happen again? What went wrong for you, Little Johnny?

### Monday, September 6, 1880
Dear Diary, may I introduce you to Joseph! Joseph arrived on Sunday. And how different Joseph seems! I pray to God-- Oh, Holy Mother, bless our child! You will understand if we don't rush Joseph out for Christening as we did John. Perhaps we were too hurried with Johnny, taking him out on Christmas Eve. We were sure our Christmas gift would heal and be perfect in every way.

### Friday, September 10, 1880
My twenty-third birthday and two boys to celebrate it with me.

### Sunday, December 19, 1880
This morning we had waffles for Johnny's first birthday. His poor little arms try to reach, then fly in all directions. But if he can get a good grip on a waffle quarter he hangs on and tears off a few bites before I have to help him. I would think he would get tired with all the wasted energy, but he keeps going. And he keeps smiling, a happy little boy in spite of all his troubles.

### Sunday, July 3, 1881
Father Ehlenberger prayed for our fallen president, James Garfield. People walk around in a gloom, the way they did after President Lincoln's assassination. He may live, but it sounds serious. So strange that General Garfield who fought in the Battle of Shiloh and the Battle of Chickamauga should be shot in peacetime.

Joseph walks now. For weeks he hung onto chairs, and seemed afraid to start on his own. I began to be afraid. Now he launches off on his own. I cry inside to see little Johnny lying there on his blanket watching his younger brother walk. Johnny makes sounds and stretches wildly in all directions, but he can't make his limbs go right. What will become of him?

## Wednesday, September 21, 1881

John said people in Spillville talked about the death of President Garfield. What will happen now with this Vice President Arthur coming in? He sounds as corrupt as any of Grant's men.

## Saturday, December 31, 1881

The last night of the week and the last night of the year.

Father Mikota has come to rest before our altar, underneath our floor. He had become a part of our church family. Now his body remains with us while his spirit soars. He has left a little scrap of his goodness where we kneel, a reminder of our own mortality. Does Saint Wenceslaus Church become like Westminster Abbey where they buried the saints in the floors and the walls?

## Wednesday, February 15, 1882

I could not write before when Charles Poshusta left us.[10] Today should have been Mama's fifteenth wedding anniversary. We had planned for today, but the angels came and got him first. He gave my mama happiness and three children. Little Barbara seemed to take it the hardest with her daddy gone. The boys hold it inside of them.

## Monday, September 10, 1883

For a long time I have neglected you, Dear Diary. My feelings hide behind my words, and my words won't come. My pencil refuses to write. I realize that it has been a long time since I have been to Mass. I can't leave Johnny at home. But when I take him with me, people look at him and look at

---

[10]January 1, 1882, Charles Poshusta died. Letter received from Cyril M. Klimesh, 12 Sept. 1992.

me with such pity. I feel as if they look at his illness and
nothing else, as if we have leprosy.

If it weren't for the newspapers bringing word from the
outside world, I would go mad. I wish I could see the ten-story
skyscraper in Chicago, but we can't go anywhere.

Little Joseph senses my shyness and has become bashful.
Sometimes when people come he will stay off in the bedroom
with Johnny, as if protecting him. At other times Joseph will
stand behind my chair. As soon as company leaves, he comes
out running.

Joey watches the windmill with fascination--anything that
turns. If he finds a few twigs, he'll build them together like a
rail fence. One day I found him with a little tower of twigs two
feet high, all woven together. It looked like an enormous
Oriole's nest upside down.

The boys' Grandpa Matej turns sixty years old this year. I
am twenty-six today.

### 1883

Today in the newspaper they told of a Dutch scientist,
Robert Koch, who can keep animals from getting anthrax. He
pricks them with a needle some way, like Dr. Pasteur with his
cowpox.

Someday they will discover how to keep babies from being
paralyzed.

### Tuesday, January 1, 1884

New Year's Day!

This year we move onto our own farm! The papers are all
signed.

### Friday, February 29, 1884

Leap Day! An extra day to pack in boxes and worry about
the weather.

Little Johnny looks at me with big wondering eyes as if to
ask, "What are you going to do with this extra day?" I tell him
I am going to scrub the floor, shake out a rug and polish the
stove. He makes wild motions with his arms, grins and
drools as if he races through the chores to help me. And I'm
sure he would if he could.

**Wednesday, March 5, 1884**

Moved at last to our own farm! We will get our mail from Ridgeway. Conover buildings huddle down the railroad track a half-hour walk--a town that somehow got cheated out of great expectations. The railroad angles up the ridge from Conover to here and on to Ridgeway. We hear its whistle and see the smoke. It puts on steam as it chugs past us. The bells of Saint Wenceslaus call to us from Spillville three miles south. America isn't the big empty place it used to be.

**Sunday, March 16, 1884**

Once again in March I feel new life within me. Why does our new little stranger's coming fill me with terror? Am I afraid I will have two babies lying on the blanket or strapped to a chair?

Johnny patiently puts up with his long days even though hours must grow long for him. It seems hardly possible he will be four this year.

**Inauguration Day, 1884**

Our new president, Grover Cleveland, gives us hope. He sounds like a good man who will continue to clean up the Spoils System. President Arthur began; Mr. Cleveland will continue. We must have no more deaths inflicted by job seekers.

**Tuesday, July 15, 1884**

I cannot stop crying even to write. Grandma Andera left us quietly yesterday. She towered above "step-grandmother" status. My real grandmother Anna Balounova died in 1849. Grandma Andera became the only Grandma to me.

We had moved out from Calmar, closer to Grandma-- thought I would see her more. Now even the windows on their house look empty. I dread to come up the driveway. Dear Diary, dear leather book, she gave you to me. I must be faithful to her memory now.

**Thursday, September 4, 1884**

Grandma and Grandpa Andera should have been married thirty-five years today.

**Wednesday, September 10, 1884**
My twenty-seventh! I wondered if I might have the baby today, and then we would always celebrate together.

**Thursday, October 2, 1884**
Dear little Francis arrived yesterday. Thank God he seems to be a healthy baby. I felt him all over to see if he had his fingers and toes.
Today I could hear Johnny and Joey squealing and gurgling at each other. When I called them, Joey pushed Johnny into our bedroom in his wheelchair. They both became as solemn as going to Mass, and wide-eyed when they first saw the baby. Then later I heard them giggling and laughing in the hallway. Francis sleeps through it all, then wakes up only to nurse.

**Saturday, October 4, 1884**
The neighbor women say I should lie in bed for days, but I feel like getting up. I have to lie here and hold the pencil and book over my head as I write. I hope I can read what I've written. Thank God for good neighbors anyway. They help with Johnny too, though I don't like for them to have to do that. He's old enough at nearly five--he should be on his own. But that, I'm beginning to think, can never be.
Father Francis Ehlenberger walked out. We have come to like Father Ehlenberger. He makes me think of what Saint Francis must have been like, barefoot, walking everywhere in his tattered robe, blessing the children. Maybe that's why I wanted to name our third boy Francis.
Francis eats and sleeps, eats and sleeps. John came in from the barn with two buckets of milk. He stood and grinned at Francis and then said, "We should have him in a brown robe like the Franciscans!"

**Monday, October 6, 1884**
The house seemed full of people yesterday. Grandpa Matej and Grandma Anna Bily were here, of course. They talk about "the new farm boy" like they did it all themselves. And then also came neighbors who hadn't been in the house before.
Francis radiates good health, but then we couldn't predict what would happen to Johnny as he grew older. John Evangelist cheered the arrival of his new brother with many

gestures and groans of joy. Joseph clings to me. He seems to want to know that I'm not going to give him up for his new brother.

Joseph stands by the foot of the bed with one hand on the bedpost and the other on Johnny's wheelchair. Joseph hasn't grown as tall as most four-year-olds, but he seems sturdy. Any more he's so heavy when I try to pick him up.

Francis reminds me how tiny a baby begins. I seem to deliver each baby easier, but I haven't the energy to lug them around I used to have. What can the matter be? I am only 27 years old.

### Wednesday, November 26, 1884

Grandpa Frantisek Andera turned eighty, wrinkled and white. The Poshusta boys call him simply, "The Old One." He lived on two continents and outlived two wives. Now he descends into bachelorhood. He's turning into an old codger without Grandma. We are all poorer without her.

### Thursday, December 25, 1884

Christmas! On our own farm, in our own home! Someday John will build a new house. I'm not afraid to be out in the country anymore.

My dear husband managed to bring back oranges for the children's stockings.

### Thursday, January 1, 1885

Dear Grandma Andera, I begin my first year without you. Even though you lived miles away, I could still feel your presence and your prayers. I have kept your diary until it was full and other diaries since, but they are all yours. I can just barely remember those first days in your house, but I remember sitting on your lap and smelling the apple butter you cooked in the fireplace and the sauerkraut in the jars. May the angels keep you safe. I know you are with me as I write.

### Wednesday, July 14, 1885

Dear Grandma Andera, a year ago you left us. Hardly a day goes by that I have not thought of you. Especially on Sundays I think we should go to see you. Today I took out one of the aprons you embroidered for me. I can see your wrinkled hands turning the thread in and out. How lovingly you did everything.

### Sunday, July 26, 1885

President Grant has marched on to eternity. His life seemed sad at the end. This great man grew poor. Even when they tried to help him with money he lost it. He spent his last months racing against death to write the story of his life.

John's father, Matej, comes out and helps to tie the oats bundles. He knows how to do it without twine. Then there are no strings in the stack. Now the younger men are talking of threshing by steam engine.

Father Ehlenberger has a funny bone. He giggles and shakes with laughter over something he sees funny--a turn of a phrase, a farmer's joke. But he'll walk off and leave the door open. We see him on the road like a vagabond. We have come to love him. Father Ehlenberger has an inventor's mind and John likes that.

### Sunday, December 27, 1885

What a week! We had Christmas and then at dinner today I realized John's birthday had sneaked up on us! He just smiled when I blurted it out. I don't know if he had thought of it or not. He used to say his birthday simply became a part of Christmas, but this year came the big one--thirtieth birthday.

I baked a cake in the afternoon and we had it for supper the way we did for Johnny's birthday a week ago last night.

### Thursday, June 17, 1886

Grandpa Frantisek died today. What a life he had, living on two continents. He came in to this life in 1809 in Hrobska Zahradka, Bohemia. He often talked about the terrible trip walking through Germany, waiting in the crowds at the dock, taking a sailing ship that would lie becalmed for days--nine weeks for the trip--food infested with worms. He always insisted that anyone coming from Bohemia should take a steamer. Of course the great steamers of today would change that. At least he got the rest of his family to come on steamers with sails. Grandma Katerina didn't talk about a terrible trip, but I've heard how on other ships they ran low on water and many suffered. Did her illness come from privation?

Anyway, without her Frantisek seemed lost. "I'm ready to go," he said. "I've lived past the Biblical three score and ten."

**Friday, September 10, 1886**
My twenty-ninth birthday.  It seems so long ago, Grandma, when you gave me that first book.  Now I have lived in the New World nearly a quarter of a century, but I still write for you.  You should be the first to know: I think I am with child again.  Pray for me.

I remember how dear Father Ehlenberger walked to our place on my birthday after Joseph was born.

The Canadian Pacific Railway nears completion, the newspaper says.  How it brings back memories of our trip through Canada, chugging through pine forests and watching the smoke roll off across the sky, cinders in our clothes.

**1887**
Saint Wenceslaus seems to go from one extreme to another in the age of its pastors.  Dear old Father Ehlenberger toddled on his way, leaning on his cane, and in his place has come the dashing young Father Thomas Bily.  I think that many a young maiden's heart flutters.  He speaks with a rush of enthusiasm, telling his dreams for our future--processions, music, celebrations.

I heard from those who go to Mass the story of the crippled beggar at the doorway.  He asked for alms and got legs.  How I wish Saint Paul could visit Johnny!  Johnny would like to go out into the world--and I would like to go with him.  But he remains chained to his chair and I am chained to him.  I shouldn't say that--we all love him so.  If only others could know what a bright, sweet person hides behind that twisted frame!

This year Queen Victoria celebrated her Golden Jubilee.  Imagine being in that exhausting job for fifty years!  But she has seemed to enjoy it--she and her many children.  She goes from one public meeting to another;  Johnny and I almost never.  If it weren't for the Church coming to us, we'd be like monks in the desert.

Pope Leo XIII has beatified Sir Thomas More.  I think he had courage like Saint Wenceslaus.  I must find out more about him.

How different our school will be with Professor Kovarik gone. I cannot find words to describe what his music has meant. The Sisters of Saint Benedict will have an eager bunch of young musicians.

**Sunday, April 17, 1887**
Yesterday I got my little girl at last. She seems well and whole, though she doesn't cry as much as I think she should. She has a voice, though.
The boys are thrilled. Frank wanted to pick her up and carry her around. Joseph walks around the edges of the bed, so sober and careful and protective. Johnny grins and bubbles. His arms flail out to the sides as if he too would like to hold her. Right now I'm content simply to lie in bed and cuddle her beside me.

**Saturday, September 10, 1887**
Joseph and I celebrated our birthdays this week--Monday and Saturday--Joe turned seven and starts in the second grade. I become--oh! don't say it--thirty! Joe lugs Anna around like a rag doll. He lays her in Johnny's lap, but she soon wiggles off to the floor and crawls away.

**Sunday, January 15, 1888**
The wind bites with bitter cold. John has, by now, sawed up a whole tree to keep us warm. We have heard that many people died in the storm in Nebraska and much livestock.

**Wednesday, February 29, 1888**
Leap Day.
Anna will soon be walking. She pulls herself up on chairs. Joe or Frank either one will try to take her by the hand and lead her out into the middle of the room, but she won't take the chance yet.
Tomorrow a few farmers will be moving. We are happy to have our own land, and some day a real house.

**Monday, April 16, 1888**

Tonight we had a little party for Anna when John got home from the field and in from doing chores. Anna toddled out with me to watch John milk old Roany. When Roany tried to turn around and look at us, Anna squealed and snuggled against me. But Roany walks in peace with her fellow cattle and with us--a mild-tempered old shorthorn.

After supper we brought out the cake and put a candle on it. Johnny made as much noise as Anna did.

**Corpus Christi, June 1888**

What a beautiful procession, the girls with their ruffled dresses, the boys all spruced up. With all the flowers there came a wonderful fragrance. Father Bily processed with the Blessed Sacrament. They made chapels from flowers strung on wire. Some day we will build tiny outdoor chapels, he says.

Father Bily really has us going. Plans move ahead to have the colored glass windows put into Saint Wenceslaus. Cousin Charlie Andera will mount them into frames.

**Wednesday, December 19, 1888**

John Evangelist clapped his hands over the nine-candle cake! Oh, Johnny! How the good Lord gives him grace to stay sweet. He teaches us all about patience. He gives fresh meaning to the word *evangel*. If only others could understand.

# 3.
# Children, Dvorák
## *1889-1899*

**1889**

The lovely stained glass windows glow with a holy light! Colored spots drape over the pews. Charles insisted I come in for a personal tour while Johnny stayed out with the boys. I brought Anna. The windows make me cry--so beautiful! Anna, the two-year-old, insisted on placing her little hands on the different colors. I think each color must have a different temperature. John laughs at me.

The German window given by Saint Clement's Church people makes our church complete. We have a reminder of where the older folks used to go before they built Saint Wenceslaus.

**Monday, July 8, 1889**

Dear God, forgive me. I worked in the garden too long and left Johnny in the house alone. His stomach had been upset, but I thought he was better. He always tells me in time, but I was out of earshot this time. As soon as I opened the house door I knew. And I had thought I'd just hoe one more row. That was wrong. I pray God to forgive me as Johnny seems to do.

**29**

**Thursday, September 5, 1889**

Joe reached nine today. He doesn't grow as fast as the other children, but he's stocky and well built. He has another year to go in school. They'll miss him from the ball team.

To the west of us, several states are coming into the Union: North and South Dakota, Montana and Washington. I will never see those places. But, then, tree-covered hills are my favorite, such as we had in Bohemia. These lands to the west have few trees they say.

Father Bily says good land waits for homesteading in South Dakota, for those who are willing to live in a sod house. But we could never travel with Johnny. He will keep us in civilized country.

**1890**

So many have died with the influenza. We have lost dear ones in this community. They have it over in Europe too. I worry so about the children--especially Johnny. How could he survive? Our guardian angel keeps us isolated.

West of us more states come into the Union--Idaho and Wyoming. We here in Iowa can no longer claim to be on the frontier.

The newspaper John brought home told how doctors at Johns Hopkins University did surgery wearing rubber gloves. How could they feel their way or do delicate sewing? How could I handle a needle and thread if I had to wear gloves? Not as many socks would get darned.

But, I think that if women were allowed to go to medical school, we would have fewer women die giving birth. More women are for strict cleanliness and keeping bedside fever away would make all the difference. I would go to medical school if I could go to school. I would spend a lifetime, if necessary, finding out what happened to Johnny.

**Thursday, April 16, 1891**

Anna ran as hard as she could go from the house to the barn. She ran out and brought Joe and Frank in from milking. She wanted them to see her gingerbread birthday cake with four candles.

Frank has been whittling and made a doll for her as a surprise. Hard to keep it from her! He had to wait until after her bedtime to work on it. Joe figured out a base so the doll can stand up on the shelf. The feet have little pegs on the bottom which fit into the stand. Now the boys insist that I make a Czech costume to go with it.

The newspaper John brought also says that a Dr. Dubois has found man bones thousands of years old. It makes one wonder how long we humans have been here. Of course, from the description it sounds more like an ape than a man.

### Saturday, December 19, 1891

John Evangelist's excitement grew all day. We lit one candle for him and put it beside a bowl of tapioca pudding--his favorite. We had him with us by the table as we ate. Then Joe brought in the gallon bucket of maple syrup ice cream from the clothesline. John says, "The newspapers talk about it being the rage in the cities. We have everything we need--Old Roany's milk and cream, our own maple syrup and Grandma's vanilla!" We hung it on the line overnight with a lid on to keep the birds out. It stayed frozen all day--frozen enough we had to dig out the ice flakes and mash them with a knife. After I fed Johnny his first bowl, he threw his arms about and made the happiest sounds. He can be made happy with such little things.

The boys worked together on a jumpity jack which hangs from the ceiling near Johnny. If he can get his hands on the string, he pulls it and jumpity's legs and arms fly up and down. Then Johnny laughs in his own special way. He knows he's too old for such a toy, but he loves to have his brothers do things with him.

Anna sewed the hems on a pillowcase for him and even embroidered JEB on it.

### Thursday, January 21, 1892

Our thirteenth anniversary. The Good Lord sends us sun and the rain. Sometimes I cry like the rain, and then I think how many thanks we have to give.

### Summer 1892

Pope Leo has spoken for the working people. John told how Father Bily read from the encyclical, *Rerum Novarum*. Workers are so often ignored. The iron and steelworkers strike. They get attention but also anger. John often remembers the terrible days of working on the railroad in

New York. When he worked out of Calmar it wasn't so bad because everyone knows each other out here.

### Saturday, October 1, 1892

Frank's eighth birthday! Lots of talk about having President Cleveland come back for another term. He can pick up where he left off. Mr. Harrison hasn't done much. John says we need a stronger money system. The farmers work all year, grow grain and cattle, and then the money we are paid isn't worth much.

Word from Bohemia is that Joseph Kovarik has become friends with the music composer, Antonin Dvorák. Such a short time ago Joseph was a little boy singing in his father's choir and playing violin in the orchestra. Now his father teaches college--an important professor--and Joe studies in Bohemia.[11]

### Sunday, December 25, 1892

Christmas on Sunday. John has been keeping a surprise for us for several weeks and today he brought it out: a tin can of pineapple. We all kept tasting until it was gone. I had talked first of keeping it so we could have a little each day, but no worry about that now.

Frank found a picture of a pineapple and carved his version of it on a board. He made it look so round-like, with the edges curving right into the board. Frank said, "That jackknife from my grandfather gives me ideas like it has a mind of its own--the best present I ever got!" He whittles so quickly.

### March 1893

Grover Cleveland inaugurated! Now we should have a return to good business management in government.

---

[11]Upon invitation of Jeannette M. Thurber, Dvorák left Prague September 15, 1892, and sailed from Bremerhaven on the liner Saale. Accompanying him were his wife, daughter Otilia, son Antonin and his new acquaintance, Joseph J. Kovarik of Spillville. . . . October 21, 1892, Antonin Dvorák conducted his first concert booked by Mrs. Thurber at Carnegie Hall in which he rendered his three new overtures, in *Nature*, *Carnival* and *Othello*. Dr. Jan Lowenback, *Joseph Jan Kovarik, Dvorák's American Secretary*.

**Saturday, April 16, 1893**
 Anna woke us all up this morning. Six years old! She bounced around in the kitchen. What? No birthday cake? I told her we had to get up first. She would be ready to start school right now if we would let her, but she will have to wait until fall.
 Joseph has been out of school more than a year now, but he says he's going to go with her to school. Frank, of course, can do that. He's a sturdy eight-year-old and will be nine when he goes to fourth grade this fall. Joe wants to protect Anna from everything. She'd never get a scratch on her if he could help it.

*The Ridgeway Recorder*
 VISITORS TO THE FAIR, THE RAILWAY DEPOTS WHERE THOUSANDS OF STRANGERS FROM ALL PARTS OF THE WORLD WILL ARRIVE--SOME INFORMATION AS TO LODGINGS.[12]

*Postville Graphic*
 "*The Ridgeway Recorder*: More than a dozen ways to break a leg, and a Waucoma man got his busted in a singular way last week. He was doing some chores in the barn where there were several head of steers, and one of them being ugly, chased Mr. Scalley into the manger where he tried to defend himself by kicking the brute, and in some way caught his leg between some boards, when the steer ran against him breaking his leg just below the knee."[13]

 Charles Andera has the Corpus Christi chapels almost done. They stand like the little wayside grottos they have in Europe--places where travelers can rest and pray. Our children are travelers.

**Tuesday, June 5, 1893**
 Such a lot of buzzing in Spillville about the new family that moved into Jacob Schmidt's house for the summer! Dr.

_____

 [12]"Visitors to the Fair," *The Ridgeway Recorder*, n.d. May 1893, n.p., n.c.

 [13]"More Than a Dozen Ways to Break a Leg," *Postville Graphic*, n.d. May 1893, n.p., n.c.

Dvořák, Joseph Kovarik's friend and teacher from New York
and Bohemia, came over from the train at Calmar with his
wife and his six children! There came a couple of other
women too, to help out, I think. To the adults he's known as Dr. Dvořák, the famous
composer. But to the children he's known as the father of six.
The boys wonder whether the young Dvořáks will be sissies
since they are from the big city.

John came home late from town. He'd been watching his
father play Darde in the saloon with Dr. Dvořák and John
Klimesh and old John Kovarik. That card game from
Bohemia hasn't caught on with the young people but the old
timers like to play. Maybe it will spark the youngsters'
interest now.

**Tuesday, June 27, 1893**

What a month this has been! They tell me about Dr.
Dvořák making that pipe organ sing and dance. Father Bily
inspires everyone with his sermons. Of course, he's happy
with the completion of the chapels in time for Corpus Christi.
Father Bily has worked for all the years since he's been here
for a Corpus Christi festival like we had this month.

Then, today Dr. Dvořák played for Rosa Hayek's
wedding to John Kinkor. Such music! Now I know the
meaning of *radost*--joy. I wish I could convey to Johnny the
joy of the music. But he had to stay home with Joe. Oh, my
*kojenec*, my baby! Will he ever get to be a grownup?

> *The Ridgeway Recorder*
> "THE WORLD'S FAIR FOR FIFTEEN CENTS. Upon
> receipt of your address and fifteen cents in postage stamps,
> we will mail you prepaid our souvenir *Portfolio of the
> World's Columbian Exposition.*"[14]

**Tuesday, September 5, 1893**

The boys have been working on a fence post near the
windmill, carving a head and shoulders out of the top of it.
They had gone out ahead of me this morning to milk cows,

---

[14]"The World's Fair for Fifteen Cents," *The Ridgeway Recorder*, 18
Jul. 1893, n.p., n.c.

then stopped to take a slice or two out of the fence post. I called out and said, "Joseph! You are thirteen today." He said, "Yeah, I know," without hardly looking up. He was penciling out areas that Frank would carve out. John says the boys could use their time better hoeing the cockleburs out of the corn rows. "That fence post," he says, "will now be too short, once some cow breaks the head off rubbing against it."

It looks like what the boys meant it to be--President Cleveland. Of course, Cleveland isn't too hard to depict with his walrus moustache, thick neck and balding head.

Joe and his dad will be busy with cornpicking in another month and Frank and Anna will be in school. Then they won't have time for any extras.

### 1894

Father Bily has gone back to Tabor, South Dakota, and in his place comes Father Chmelar. How we will miss Father Bily! He had a flair about him. Dvorák's coming seemed so appropriate with Father Bily here. We had music and more music. The menfolk came home singing.[15]

Now, Father Chmelar has the men starting the "Workmen for the World" club. Pope Leo's *Rerum Novarum* takes effect--finding feet and hands to carry Christ's concern.

### Saturday, July 14, 1894

Dear Grandma Andera, you have been in heaven ten years today. For two years Grandpa lingered alone. I have still the memory of your apple strudel, how you pounded and spread it out and how you let me sprinkle the apples and nuts before you rolled it up. You helped me grow up to be a woman.

### 1895

Now they are sending words through the airwaves! No more telegraph poles! We will get words and even music like angels from the sky.

---

[15]Dvorák's *Symphony No. 5 in E Minor* introduced by the New York Philharmonic Orchestra Dec. 15, 1893. New York newspapers proclaimed that never had any composer had such triumph. Reception a "magnificent success."

**Monday, November 18, 1895**

John went to Decorah today to clear up that land deal. The Brekke's are such agreeable neighbors.

**Friday, December 27, 1895**

We celebrated John's fortieth birthday tonight with oyster stew. He said, "I used to work ten hours a day without ever getting tired. Now I feel like I'm getting old."

Dr. Dvorák went back to Prague. We thought he might make one more trip to Spillville. We are too far west.

**Thursday, February 27, 1896**

Charles and Barbara Andera had a baby boy yesterday. I imagine Charles singing as he works in his carpenter shop this morning, and the neighbor women are coming in to see Barbara. I pray to God that he is a healthy baby! They have had so much sadness, losing baby Charles and little Albert. She lives in town anyway--in Spillville, surrounded by people.

William McKinley will be our new president! He knows what illness means with his sick wife. Maybe he will have special understanding for our country's illnesses.

**Saturday, February 29, 1896**

Leap Year with the extra day, the bonus! I used it to scrub floors and clean out the pantry. The boys went in to Wenzil Baliks to get the plow sharpened and took some cultivator shovels along too. They like to watch him work that forge. Wouldn't be surprised if one of the boys became a blacksmith. Maybe they can plow the garden next month.

**March 1896**

I brought clothes in from the line this noon and Johnny plunged his face into the fresh linen towels and smiled. Nothing smells any better than freshly washed clothes brought in from the line.

**1897**

Queen Victoria's Diamond Jubilee. She had a family before I was born and still she reigns. It makes me feel as if I'm not so old.

**Monday, January 3, 1898**

Father Chmelar died. It makes me remember hearing of how Dr. Dvořák played dirges for Joe Cibuzar's funeral. Dr. Dvořák made death seem so majestic. I wish he could have been here to play for Father Chmelar. We have come to love the good old priest because he cared so much for us and for working people. He was an organizer.

Father Gajdousek has spoken kind words for Father Chmelar.

**Saturday, January 21, 1899**

John and I have been married twenty years. It hardly seems possible. We married during the coldest month of the year so our anniversaries have usually been cold.

**Sunday, February 12, 1899**

I pity the children. They should stay home from school when the weather turns bitter like this. When it's more than thirty below it takes a long time to get the schoolroom warm. The little ones huddle by the stove. The inkwells freeze. The drinking water bucket has to be set on top of the stove. When I went out to gather eggs at noon, I found most of them cracked from freezing.

**July 1899**

Today we put down cabbage for sauerkraut. The smell fills the house. Some say they don't like the smell of cabbage, but I like it. But then, I slice up a few of the first summer apples and layer them with the kraut for a sweeter taste. Maybe that makes our kraut smell sweeter.

**Sunday, September 10, 1899**

My forty-second. My last birthday of this century. The boys will soon be in the cornfields.

**November 1899**

Today we took the bricks off the wooden lids on the sauerkraut crocks. We only had a little spoilage this year. I think the apples help. Anyway the kraut tastes sweet and mild. And what a wonderful smell.

### Tuesday, December 19, 1899

Johnny turned twenty years old. It seems impossible that he has lived like this for so long. If we could have foreseen what was ahead of us, we might have lost courage. This must be why the Good Lord doesn't let us see our tomorrows.

And yet, Johnny stays so sweetly dispositioned he makes up for everything. When the boys are here they help with lifting him.

### Sunday, December 31, 1899

The last day of a century! I know that today will be no different to the horses who stand looking over the fence. The cattle in the yard care not for another century--no difference just another day to all of life except us humans. The snowbirds will scavenge in the fields for grain tomorrow the same as today. But for us, a hundred years have passed.

During this century I have lived in two worlds. When this celebration comes around again, we all will have lived in two worlds and the world to come. Holy Mary, Mother of God . . . pray for us sinners.

In another year John Evangelist will come of age, but he will never get to vote. He will be an adult and yet a child in the eyes of others. He watches the birds that flutter at the window and I think he feels a kinship. I say he knows about a century turning. In some ways he's lived longer than any of us. He understands. He tells me more than I can put in words. He becomes more sombre when we talk about it. He quickly picks up my moods.

Joseph will be twenty, Frank sixteen, and Anna, bless her heart, thirteen.

May the bells ring out tonight. The bells of Saint Wenceslaus will ring in the Year of our Lord--the Century of our Lord. "We are not alone," says our new Father Dostal. "The century belongs to Christ. For this we celebrate."

I get carried away with writing. But I have found that I can buy another leather-covered book and go on. Each one has Grandma Andera's love in it, because she gave me more than a book. She gave me an idea--gave me the pages of my life.

# 4.

# Farming, Carpentering, Carving
## *1900-1909*

**Wednesday, February 28, 1900**

It seems that we should be having another leap year since it has been four years. But as the almanac explained, we give up that extra day at the end of February since we changed a century. We give up a *den* [day] and gain a *sto* [century]!

**Sunday, September 16, 1900**

Today at Mass Father Dostal prayed for President McKinley's soul and for his family. We are his family. The whole nation mourns.

I'm sorry the assassin was Polish. Our cousins across the border bow their heads in shame.

Frank outlined a picture of the president on a piece of maple and began gouging. By supper time you could see

**39**

McKinley's face emerging from the wood. Joe watched him, admiringly, and said we should hang that on the wall or build it into a bookcase.

### Saturday, January 19, 1901

Grandma Anna Bily lies dead. She "belongs to the ages," as Seward said of President Lincoln. Anna cried the way I cried when I left my family in Bohemia. I wonder if Anna will remember her grandma Bily the way I remember my [step] grandma Andera? She should; she's thirteen.

### Sunday, January 20, 1901

John said Father Dostal prayed for Grandma Anna today when he celebrated Mass. Our Anna takes her death to heart, losing her namesake.

Father Dostal seems--I shouldn't say it, but--almost like a little pudgy-cheeked boy. After all, a young-looking thirty-year-old seems hardly like my father.

### Saturday, January 26, 1901

Through the weekend Grandma Bily's body lay in their parlor. Such weather! But, with embalming and it being so cold, she changed not at all, looking sweetly asleep.

It has been a long hard wait for her and us. Now that we have laid her to rest, we can rest. She was seventy-six.

Then we learned that Queen Victoria died only three days after Grandma Bily. Both were queens in a way.

Grandpa Matej seems as robust as ever. I think he will live to be a hundred.

### May 1901

Joe brought in a bunch of lilac blossoms for me to put in water. Johnny grinned, rubbed his nose with the back of his hand and waved toward the bouquet. I'm glad for everything he can enjoy--in this case fragrance of lilacs.

### Thursday, September 5, 1901

Today Joe gets his long-awaited twenty-first birthday. This year he gets to vote!

**1902**

The boys are taking turns reading the new Leonardo da Vinci biography. They read all the time on winter evenings when they aren't whittling.

People are talking about the phonograph with the singing of Enrico Caruso.

**August 1902**

Today the boys burned a patch of Indian crazy weed. Joe worked on the downwind side with the wet burlap sack and buckets of water to keep the fire from getting over into the fence line. But Frank said Joe worked too long in that thick white smoke. When Joe finally got the fire stamped out he wasn't the same Joe. "He laughed sort of silly," Frank said. "Joe would see a stick on the ground and step high to get over it, like it was a log instead of a stick. He talked crazy and I thought he was putting on, but it wasn't a joke." Frank said, "Joe wouldn't even help put out the last of the other fire." Frank brought him back to the house. Even at supper Joe had that faraway look like he wasn't even with us. I think they should plow those weeds out in the spring instead of burning them in the fall.

**Monday, January 19, 1903**

The men were in Decorah today, finishing up the purchase of more land. Land gets harder to buy, and we had to pay $3,990 cash for this. I wonder if it will ever pay for itself. But, the boys have to have land if they are going to farm.

Sometimes I think Joe and Frank are going to be carpenters, and then they talk farming. When they're farming they talk carpentering. Joe has spent a lot of nights studying a book that came with his carpenter's square. They have built farm buildings at the neighbors.

I tell them, "If you want to make money, build houses." They say, "No more houses." I think building our farm home broke their hearts. They couldn't put all the trimmings on that they found in that *Palliser's New Cottage Homes* book. John said that plan book had a good house they could go ahead and build, but it was all dressed up for city folks. He said the boys had to cut it down to size.

**Monday, February 16, 1903**

Everything frozen up. The boys say that some of the waterpipes in Spillville have frozen five and a half feet in the ground. Our thermometer showed 42 below. If we only can keep our well going! The boys can haul water to the livestock. The groundhog promised six more weeks of winter and he's keeping his promise.

**Saturday, December 19, 1903**

Tonight we sang around the table for John Evangelist. John got out his old violin. Johnny seemed so happy and tried to sing along with us. I'm sure they heard in heaven and understood what he sang.

This was the year dear old Pope Leo XIII died and they elected Pope Pius X. Pope Pius will be a good leader for peace among the nations. There are already too many bloodstains on this century.

Joe and Frank were excited this year about the coast-to-coast automobile race. They've been studying pictures of the automobiles and making drawings.

Father Peter Kloss, our new pastor, walks around like a bean stalk on legs. Thin and intense, he crackles with ideas. He wants a new rectory and more land for the church and cemetery.

**Monday, February 29, 1904**

After an eight-year wait, we have another Leap Year, an extra day in February. Think of all the women who have had to wait this long to pop the question! There! I've had my joke for the day.

**May 1904**

This morning I heard Frank whistling part of *Humoresque*. We have grieved the loss of Dr. Dvořák since hearing of his death the first of this month--his funeral became a day of mourning in Bohemia. We've had our own special link with him, and I suppose some of us secretly hoped we might get him back for one more visit. He wasn't so old-- only sixty-two. But he didn't even come back while he finished out his years in New York.

**Thursday, September 8, 1904**

Dr. Dvorák would have been sixty-three years old today. We talked about it at Joe's birthday on Monday. Then my birthday comes this weekend.

**November 1904**

President Roosevelt re-elected! At first we wondered about him. We thought he'd be all for war. He's not that way. He seems to love his family and he cares about the land and rural people. After all, he's a cowboy and has lived in the West.

**Monday, February 13, 1905**

Cold creeps in like death. The boys spend all their time getting feed to the livestock and keeping stock watered. Thank God the well hasn't frozen yet. The boys packed lots of straw around it, which may have saved it. More than thirty below. We are using up our wood. The boys will have to cut more trees if this keeps up.

**April 1905**

Ah! The first wild asparagus! The boys brought bunches from along the roadside where the prairie grass still grows. I love the smell of asparagus cooking.

**Tuesday, September 5, 1905**

Joe's twenty-fifth birthday.

**Sunday, September 10, 1905**

The boys have their pegs out again, for shucking corn. Every year at my birthday they start off on the long job of walking the corn rows. Then they come in at night with raw ankles from sandburs. They've walked many miles up and down the hills.

**Sunday, October 1, 1905**

We will have three men voters in the family this November. Frank says, "I have twenty-one notches on my Dan'l Boone rifle this year." Twenty-one years. I think Johnny would vote too if we had any way to get him down there and write for him. The election officials would think we were fit for the asylum.

**Wednesday, December 27, 1905**

We used to think that fifty year olds were old-timers. Now I'm married to one. Frank Benda made John a pair of shoes. That will be his birthday present. John says he can put in as hard a day's work as any of the younger ones, in spite of saying he was tired when he was forty. And he can stack bundles better than most of them. So many nowadays set up shocks in the field and let the threshing machine do the work. Of course the men have to pitch bundles on the hayracks and throw them into the separator. But John says nothing will withstand a bad storm like a good stack of bundles, not even a wooden barn.

**November 1906**

Dear Diary, I have neglected you too long. None of my children seem interested in marriage. I wonder if they worry about what happened with John Evangelist. Are they afraid to marry?

Father Broz has arrived to take over the parish. He seems gruff, but the menfolk like that. The women will go along.

How I long to be out of this house sometimes, but I cannot find a way to take Johnny. People look at him and me and seem to blame us as if we did something wrong. How long will we endure our prisons?

The boys are carving beautiful pieces, learning from their books--carving leaves and flowers. Sometimes the wood splits and they have to start all over. But, they have patience. Anna and I darn socks, do embroidery or hook rugs. Frank whittles and carves while holding the work in his lap. He has only slipped and cut himself twice.

**December 1906**

Joe made a pair of skiis for the Brekke boys. Frank helped him boil the ends so they could turn up. They even put the groove down the bottom.

**January 1907**

The Brekke boys had been sliding down hills with their skiis and now they're pulling each other on horseback. Those Morgans of the Brekkes can run like race horses. Then the skier swings out in wide arcs on the long lariat rope. It's like playing "crack the whip" and the skier gets way out in front of the horse part of the time. Joe says it works like a pendulum, the skier swinging back and forth behind the horse.

The boys have been at the church part of the day, watching the Chapel of Our Lady of Lourdes being built into the southeast corner of the church. They would like to have been in on the designing of it, I think, but they were too shy.

Joe and Frank come home and work over their carving books every night. Mother said my cousin Charlie always studied books on carpentry when he was a boy. Always better ideas! Of course Joe and Frank love to watch Charlie carve out the forms for the grave markers. Charlie tells about the foundry where he sends his forms, but they aren't interested in the ironwork. They're like Charlie; they love wood.

### Tuesday, September 10, 1907

My children certainly remembered me on my fiftieth birthday. Anna baked a cake. Johnny has been excited all day. He knew something was coming up so I picked up his excitement. Tonight after supper and poppy seed cake, Joe and Frank brought out a box. Inside they had a beautifully carved plaque of the Holy Family! I didn't recognize it at first as coming from Frank's school desk.

Oh! It was marvelous! You could see Mary and Joseph and the baby Jesus in Egypt.

Then I recognized the wood from Frank's old school desk top. Last spring the board of directors voted to give Frank that old desk he had cut up so much. Nobody could use it anyway and it had sat off in a corner of the school with books on it. Now they're getting new desks so they said Frank might as well have it. White maple! Now we will figure out which wall to hang it on.

### Saturday, February 29, 1908

Happy Leap Day! To all the babies born on the extra day, special blessings!

### 1908

Father Broz leads us at a breathless pace. They've torn up the floor of the church and overlaid with tile. New pews.

We read with horror about the zeppelin disaster. Frank had already carved a frieze of the lighter-than-air craft, so when it went down, he felt as if something of his own went down too.

**March 1908**
The boys bought some ponderosa pine for their outdoor buildings. Joe says the tree trunks smell like vanilla. What I sensed most was the piney turpentine.

**Tuesday, April 16, 1908**
Anna didn't wake us up early on her birthday the way she used to. But she did awaken early, she said, and lay there watching a bug crawl up the window screen outside the house. She said she tried to remember what she had done on each of her birthdays and remembered best the ones where she was allowed to eat on top of the stepladder or on top of the kitchen counter. I had forgotten about that. My mother let me do that a time or two.

The boys tease Anna about getting old since she turned twenty-one. They say she's becoming an old maid. I say they shouldn't talk. Joseph will be twenty-eight this year and Frank twenty-four. In the Old Country they didn't think anything of the men marrying when they were older. In this country when they are twenty-one they think it's high time. Johnny just grins and seems to enjoy their teasing each other.

Anna says she should be able to vote the way the men do. She acts quiet most of the time, but she has strong ideas.

Joe looks over his builders' catalogs and plans buildings he would like to build. But now it's corn planting time.

**1909**
North Pole! Go straight north as far as I came from Bohemia long ago! The boys have followed the expedition every step of the way, I think. Robert Edwin Peary would have had two extra team members if he had asked Joe and Frank.

Mrs. Brekke's father, Mr. Anderson, died. They say he liked to work with wood.

Bust of Joseph Spillman [Spielmann], founder of Spillville, Iowa, from the Bily Brothers Statuary Clock. Photo by S.K. Hutchinson.

L. to R. Mary Bily and Anna Bily.

Bust of Antonin Dvořák from the Bily Brothers' Statuary Clock. Photo by
S.K. Hutchinson

Charles Andera.

John Evangelist Bily.

L. to R. Mary Bily, Frank Bily and Anna Bily preparing cabbage for sauerkraut.

Joseph Bily with horses.

Joseph Bily.

John Bily residence.

Bily carving of the Holy Family.

Anna Bily.

Joseph Bily with carpenter's square and plane.

Bily carving of Madonna and Child.

Bily carving of Westminster Abbey. Photo by S.K. Hutchinson.

Face of Bily Brothers' Creation Clock.

"Hall Clock made by Bily Bros., Ridgeway, Iowa." Unidentified black and white postcard, circa 1920.

Frank Bily.

L. to R.  John Bily and his brother Frank Bily.

L. to R.  Joseph Bily and Frank Bily.

L. to R.  Joseph Bily and Frank Bily.

Display advertisement for the Chimes of Normandy Clock, plan number 575, offered by H.L. Wild in *Wild's Latest Designs and Price List of Scroll Sawyers Materials.*

Clock face of the Bily Brothers' Grand Tower Clock. Photo by S.K. Hutchinson.

Frank Bily with the Bily Brothers' Apostles' Parade Clock.

Bust of Charles A. Lindbergh from the Bilys' Lindbergh Clock.
Photo by S.K. Hutchinson.

Frank Bily with panels that would eventually be used in the Bily Brothers' American Pioneer History Clock.

Bily pocketknife display at Bily Clocks Museum, Spillville, Iowa. Photo by D. Hutchinson.

Aerial photo of the Bily Brothers farm home in Ridgeway, Iowa.

L. to R.  Back row:  Mary Andrea Bily, Anna Bily, Louis Bily, John Bily, Joseph C. Bily, Frank L. Bily.  Front row: Frank Kuboushek, Mary Kovarik Bily, Frank Bily, John Bily, Frank Bily.

It is difficult to realize how small this carving is compared to the scale of the clock which measures nearly nine feet tall. The book on the pulpit, for example, is about the same size as a couple of nickels. Bily Brothers' Apostles' Parade Clock. Photo by S.K. Hutchinson.

Old Swedish Clock restored by the Bily Brothers.  Photo by S.K. Hutchinson.

Carved bust of Mrs. William Day, one of nineteen figures and panels in the
Bily Brothers' Statuary Clock. Photo by S.K. Hutchinson.

Three of the apostles in the Bily Brothers' Apostles' Clock. Photo by S.K. Hutchinson.

Close-up view of musicians in the Bily Brothers' Statuary Clock. Photo by S.K. Hutchinson.

Mary Bily.

Native American family with bear in the Bily Brothers' On The Lookout Clock.
Photo by S.K. Hutchinson.

Close-up view of the Bily Brothers' Parade of Nations Clock.  Photo by S.K. Hutchinson.

The influence of medieval art in the great cathedrals is evident here in the squatting figure of the Bily Brothers' Paradise Clock. Photo by S.K. Hutchinson

Bily Brothers' Elizabeth Fry Clock. Photo by S.K. Hutchinson.

Bily Brothers' History of Travel Clock.   Photo by S.K.
Hutchinson.

"Pioneer Women" from the Bily Brothers'
Statuary Clock. Photo by S.K. Hutchinson.

The square-jawed, bearded blacksmith looks intently out from his momentary pause, as though interrupted by the photographer. The Bily Brothers' Village Blacksmith Clock. Photo by S.K. Hutchinson.

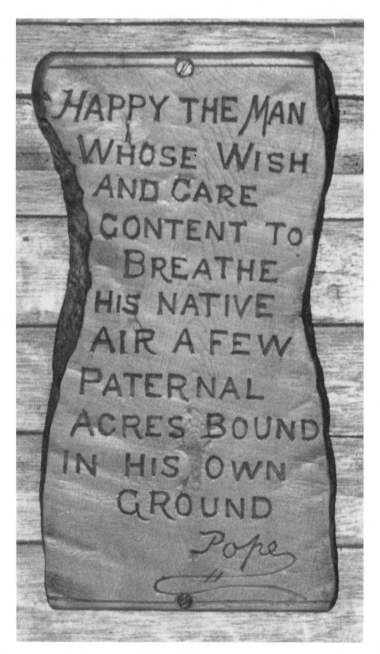

HAPPY THE MAN
WHOSE WISH
AND CARE
CONTENT TO
BREATHE
HIS NATIVE
AIR A FEW
PATERNAL
ACRES BOUND
IN HIS OWN
GROUND
*Pope*

Alexander Pope's quote is a clue to the Bilys' philosophy of life. They reversed the order of two lines. The original read, "Happy the man whose wish and care, A few paternal acres bound, Content to breathe his native air, In his own ground." Bilys' Village Blacksmith Clock.

# 5.
# Scrollwork Clocks, WW I
## *1910-1919*

**Sunday, April 24, 1910**

Peaple have been talking about the comet all weekend. The scientists say nothing will hurt us. But they also say there are poisonous gases in the tail and we're going to go through the tail. Well, I am ready to die if the Good Lord calls. But what about the children of the world?

**Thursday, May 19, 1910**

We're supposed to be going through the tail of the comet right now. This may be the last time I write in this book, and there will be nobody to read it. However, no one seems to be getting sick. We can't see the comet because either clouds cover the sky or moonlight keeps us from seeing that pale feathery tail in the night sky. The important thing: nobody seems to be getting sick.

**Sunday, May 22, 1910**
The comet they've talked so much about hangs like a long streamer in the southwest. They say it flies away faster than the fastest-flying airplane.
Mark Twain died. He had said he was born the year of the comet and he would die when it returned. They said it glowed brightly the night he died. He had kept his promise. We claim him for Iowa since he lived and worked at Keokuk and his mother lived there.

**Monday, September 5, 1910**
I baked prune kolaches for Joe's thirtieth today.
The excitement over Saint Wenceslaus's Golden Jubilee has been building for two years and threatens to reach a fevered pitch. With the new floor in the church, new pews, new wide sidewalk and Charles Andera's new arch over the walk they feel spiffed up.
Our Norwegian neighbors are talking about Roald Amundsen going to the South Pole! Much to think about.

**Wednesday, September 28, 1910**
Sunny, pleasant day for the golden jubilee! The boys said there was standing room only in Spillville. The women cooked so many geese and ducks there won't be anything but feathers left in the country!
Joe grins and says, "That church wasn't even twenty years old when I was born." He likes to imitate an old bachelor. He even walks like his old grandpa Matej.

**Wednesday, December 7, 1910**
The boys keep such careful records. I noticed on Joe's copy of the *American Carpenter and Builder* he had written "Received December 7th, 1910, 2:15 P.M."

**Sunday, January 8, 1911**
The boys came back from Spillville and said Dr. Hennessey was in town.

**Wednesday, October 11, 1911**
Poor old Grandpa Matej. I'm afraid he's not long for this world. He lives for his plum brandy. He gets knocked out and his daughter has to go find him. Well, she's the one who

gives it to him in the first place.  That homemade brandy should be for sipping only!

[Clipping found between the pages.]
*Decorah Republican* - from *Gutenberg Press*
Walter Smock had a very narrow escape from what might have proved to be a serious if not fatal accident, Tuesday, while assisting in putting a rope on a fractious heifer which he and Tony were going to lead. They had the rope already fastened to the animal when it started to run and in doing so ran around Mr. Smock, throwing him to the ground and wrapping the rope around his body and neck and dragging him for a considerable distance.  Had it not been for the fact that the stockyards gate was closed so the animal couldn't get away he would no doubt have been killed before he could have been released from his plight.[16]

### Saturday, November 11, 1911
Joe and Frank came in a little before noon.  Joe pulled his watch out and said, "Eleven, eleven, eleven, eleven" and then laughed.  "This is the eleventh month, eleventh day of 1911 at eleven o'clock."  Joe is always the one who likes numbers. He carries his carpenter's square around and shows how to do the arithmetic of carpentering with it--figuring what angles to cut rafters and so on.

### Thursday, November 16, 1911
Grandpa Matej [Mathias] Bily died today.  We figured he was eighty-eight years old.  He has outlived Grandma Anna ten years and almost ten months.

### Saturday, November 18, 1911
Father Broz summed up Grandpa's life.  I'm glad Father Broz was here because Grandpa liked and respected him.

*The Decorah Republican*
Another of our pioneers, Mathias Bily, died Thursday last after a few days' illness at the home of his daughter, Mrs. John Poshusta.  He was 89 years old.  Funeral was held

16"_____," *The Decorah Republican*, 19 Oct. 1911, n.p., n.c.

Saturday at the Saint Wenceslaus church. Interment at the cemetery adjoining.[17]

Father Bily came from New Prague, Minnesota, last week.

**Tuesday, December 19, 1911**
Johnny's birthday. They say that Jesus was thirty-two or thirty-three years old at the time of his crucifixion. Johnny has now reached thirty-two years old, hung in his chair for three decades. But the light of his smile seems to fill the room. I'm glad we called him John Evangelist.

**Friday, January 12, 1912**
So cold today everything froze up. The boys chop a hole in the horse tank, but the hole closes up again. The trees pop like gunshots. John said it was over 40 below zero this morning.

**Thursday, February 29, 1912**
The boys tried boiling linseed oil today out in the shop and the smell even gets into their clothes. I can tell it when they come into the house.

**Wednesday, March 20, 1912**
The Brekkes were talking about Roald Amundsen, the Norwegian explorer, finding the South Pole. There was a story in the *Decorah Posten*, their Norwegian newspaper.

**Tuesday, September 10, 1912**
My birthday today. Frank and Joe surprised me with a beautiful plaque, like the one from that desk top the teacher had brought from school. Frank did most of the carving, Joe said, but I know Joe did the planning and drawing out of the picture because I ran across it when I was cleaning. Its beauty touches me. I take back everything I ever said about their messes!

---

17"_____," *The Decorah Republican*, 23 Nov. 1911, n.p., n.c.

### Wednesday, September 18, 1912

The boys moved the toilet a little closer to the house today. It took awhile digging a new hole, but they didn't want to have to move it again soon. Now it won't be so far walking this winter.

### Sunday, December 1, 1912

Joseph studies his carpentering books. He makes every cut and drives each nail with care--such a good carpenter, the neighbors say. He won't allow his hammer to dent the wood when he's driving a nail. But, Joseph doesn't sell himself. Even when someone asks him about building a barn or a hog house, he's almost apologetic. Then he comes home and feels bad about it. He reads and reads and dreams about the buildings he'd like to build.

### Thursday, December 12, 1912

Today when the boys came in to eat I got Joe back. I had just brought some mashed potatoes to the table when I pointed up to the grandfather's clock. I said to Joe: "Twelve, twelve, twelve, twelve."

Joe looked mystified and then thought I was scolding him. He said, "What's the matter, did you want us in here earlier?"

When I pointed to the calendar he tumbled to what I was saying. He said, "Frank! Johnny! Anna! This is the twelfth day of the twelfth month of the year 1912, and it's twelve noon!" And then, as if in answer, the clock struck out the hour. We had a good laugh over that one.

### Thursday, December 26, 1912

Joseph assembled a rubber stamp out of the stamp set we gave him. It says:

"JOS. C. BILY,
SPILLVILLE, IOWA
CARPENTER AND PLAN SPECIALIST"

That's what he'd like to do, full time. He likes to do the planning as much as the construction. Maybe this next year he'll put himself out more and get the jobs.

### Tuesday, January 21, 1913

John and I have been married thirty-four years. We hardly celebrated at all. We feel lucky to be alive and feel well. What will become of Johnny when we are gone? Joe and Frank seem more interested in tinkering than farming.

This winter the boys have been making a big complicated clock from plans that Joe adapted out of a magazine. They call it the "Creation Clock." It has old Father Time and there will be angels up overhead. I can hear the thump, thump, thump of their saw going--the saw that they made out of my old treadle sewing machine.

One of the neighbors found a skunk under his house and shot it with his twelve gauge. His wife said the smell went all through their clothes so they didn't feel like they could go anywhere for days. Others can smell it long after the victim can.

### Wednesday, April 16, 1913

We celebrated Anna's twenty-sixth today. The "Creation Clock" sends its comforting ticktock all through the house. Frank says he made this clock for Anna with old Father Time marking off her years. She acts miffed, puts her hands on her hips and takes a kick at him as if to say, "So there, Smarty." But good fun flashes in her eyes.

Joe says the angels hovering overhead represent her, so she smiles, nods extravagantly at Frank.

They do love their little sister.

### Monday, July 21, 1913

The Brekkes have a baby boy. Dr. Hennessey came out from Calmar. They say he has a birthday tomorrow. Dear man! Doc travels all over to these country places. At least it's not wintertime.

John grinned and said, "That young feller came in time to help with the oats harvest."

Well, we can laugh. He has all the signs of good health. Johnny has to fight the heat and can't even swat at a fly to hit it. But he never complains.

### Friday, September 5, 1913

Joe's birthday today. He's all excited about the building of the "Hall Clock." It will have a lot of lacey woodcuts. They ordered the movement and hands and numbers from New York.

### Saturday, December 27, 1913

John's fifty-eighth! The boys finished the "Hall Clock." This one will go in the hall between the kitchen and our bedroom. Joe built a beautiful shelf for it.

### Thursday, April 16, 1914

Anna's birthday always comes at corn planting time. The boys are finishing up their winter's carving and putting things away for the summer. They have been so busy with carpentering around the neighborhood that they haven't been able to work on their clock. With the coming of war in Europe, Frank and Joe have been thinking more about this great free country of ours. Frank carved a figure of George Washington which will go into the archway of the "Capitol-Style Clock." But they won't get to finish it until next winter.

### June 1914

Today Frank brought me a stem of wild roses. Anna quickly mashed the stem's ends and put them in a Mason quart jar. When I hold the rose blossoms close to Johnny, he grins and gets a heavenly look on his face.

### Thursday, September 10, 1914

The boys have been picking corn all day. They go out at sunup. I can hear the ears of corn hitting the bang boards when I step outside.

I am fifty-seven today. In exactly three weeks Frank will be thirty, and next year John will be sixty. I remember when we thought people this age were ancient. And, we are--I can feel myself withering up. I'm sure I've lost an inch or more.

### Friday, December 18, 1914

Tonight we had oyster stew to celebrate the end of corn picking.

### Saturday, December 19, 1914

Johnny's birthday. We had poppy-seed kolaches, his favorite--and tapioca pudding. The boys are still working on the "Capitol-Style Clock." It seems that it has taken them so long because of the many interruptions.

### Thursday, January 21, 1915

Our thirty-sixth wedding anniversary.

Joe and Frank have finished the "Capitol-Style Clock." Joe already has big plans for the "Apostles' Clock." This famous design, they say, has been around for more than a generation. The problem will be to get wood from Europe with the war on. And they have to get it planed down to the thickness they need.

We don't know how the war affects our relatives in Bohemia. We have heard that many soldiers in the trenches are dying of lockjaw.

### Monday, January 25, 1915

This morning I heard a chickadee with its sad sing-song melody. I didn't think they would be here in cold weather.

### Monday, December 27, 1915

John's sixtieth birthday! He says he's ready to go on to eighty. We had apple pie with the last of the fall apples.

The church and rectory should be secure against the winter winds and snow since the new roofs are in place.

### Tuesday, February 29, 1916

My Grandma Andera's day. She always noticed this day and I remember to make this diary entry. I scrubbed floors and cleaned and blackened the stove.

### Sunday, April 16, 1916

Anna's twenty-ninth. She says she isn't going to be thirty, she just isn't.

The boys finished up the "Apostles' Clock" last night! It made me dizzy to look at all those little pieces. Of course, we heard the clump-clump-clump of my old sewing machine treadle which they changed into a scroll saw. Night after night they sawed those things. But the loveliness of the whole shows that every piece belongs. And such a wonderful sound. We have several clocks making music every hour with gonging and clicking and cuckooing. Johnny loves to watch the hands when they get close to the hour. He keeps looking and waiting and then tries to clap his hands when they all go off, as if each hour achieves another victory.

The smell of apple blossoms drifts in the windows.

### Sunday, May 21, 1916

Our new mail carrier, Mr. M. O. Libbey, has moved over from Route 1, Ridgeway. He's over fifty years old and was sick for about a month last year, but he said he had never been sick before and hasn't been since. So, we are hoping he can handle this route all right. The boys watch the mail closely-- especially after they have ordered something. Right now they are looking each day for a package of wood for the "Dome Clock" they'll be working on this winter. They said he always used to carry the mail with a team and wagon, but now he has a car that will scare any horse off the road. In fact you can hear him over the whole route of several miles. Looks to me like the horses would be more dependable.

### Sunday, September 10, 1916

Joe and I had our birthdays this week--he turned thirty-six last Tuesday and I fifty-nine today. Next year will be the big birthdays for Anna and me. Do we stay at nine the way Anna says? Joe chuckles at our nine-cent bargain counter ages. We deserve to be teased.

We are simply lucky to be alive. So many are dying in Europe. And then the trouble in New Mexico with Pancho Villa! I'm glad we don't live near the border.

### November 1916

Woodrow Wilson, our new president! He kept us out of war, but I'm afraid we will get into it anyway. Anyway, he supports the little countries. That's what the Czechs need now.

### Wednesday, December 27, 1916

For John's sixty-first birthday we had roast duck and mashed potatoes--his favorites.

*The Decorah Republican*
   The secretary of state announces that the official census
of Winneshiek County is 22,238, an increase of 500 over
1910.[18]

## Sunday, January 21, 1917
   Our thirty-eighth wedding anniversary.   Anna cooked
dinner.

## Monday, April 16, 1917
   In spite of her protests, Anna, our baby of the family,
admits to being thirty years old!  Anna always seemed the
perpetual child to us.  To the boys she's ever "little sister."
Tonight Frank teased her and said she's "over-the-hill."  She
gave him a dark look and pushed him against the wall.  He
said, "Look out!  You'll make me knock over a clock."  She
said, "It's you're fault, to say such things.  Anyway you're the
old bachelors."  Then they laugh and make up just like they
always did.  Johnny laughs with them when he knows they're
teasing.

## Monday, September 10, 1917
   Today the big one--sixty!  Frank turned thirty-three last
week.  If it weren't for birthdays and anniversaries I wonder
if I'd ever write to you, Dear Diary.  What do I say?  I scrubbed
floors and washed windows today?  And then, I'm so thankful
we have floors and windows.   When I think of people in
Europe I cry on the inside.

*The Decorah Republican*
   ORGANIZE TO HELP BOHEMIA--PEOPLE OF
SPILLVILLE TAKE ON NEW WAR WORK--WILL AID
CZECHS TO OBTAIN THEIR LIBERTY AND TAKE
THEIR RIGHT PLACE IN THE WORLD: The citizens of
Spillville are not satisfied in raising more than their quota of
Red Cross funds and buying more than their allotment of
Liberty bonds and War Savings stamps, but they had added
a new patriotic duty . . . assistance to the Czecho-Slovak
cause by raising funds for the Czecho-Slovak army and its
provisional government.  A branch of the Bohemian

---

[18]"_____," *The Decorah Republican*, 4 Jan. 1917, n.p., n.c.

National Alliance was started for this purpose. The first program given under its auspices was rendered Thursday, August 15, in the A.B.C.S. hall and consisted in a number of patriotic addresses and music. The first address was given by Prof. Alois F. Kovarik, Ph.D., Sc. D., of Yale University, who rendered a clear exposition of the present war aims of the allies and of the Teutons and showed by historical references to the legal position of the Czecho-Slovaks in the Austro-Hungarian Empire, and to their free and independently formed alliance in 1526 with Austria and Hungary, under the Hapsburgs, in consequence of the threatening advance of the Turks. He then pointed out the fact the Hapsburg, acting on the principle of "might is right," destroyed the Bohemian constitution, and although they were crowned as kings of Bohemia, Moravia and Silesia, they did on almost all occasions, break their oath to the Czecho-Slovak people, namely, to protect their rights and their lands. The Czecho-Slovaks however, never gave up their rights legally and when the present conflict started they were immediately on the side of the allies against Germany and Austria. Many of their citizens have been hung or shot, their property confiscated, and yet this nation is defiant even though surrounded by German cannon and bayonets. . . .[19]

*The Decorah Republican*
School commenced in the higher room of the public school, Tuesday, by S. Kruchek.[20]

*The Decorah Republican,*
IN THE GRIP OF INFLUENZA--COUNCIL ORDERS MAYOR TO CLOSE SCHOOLS, CHURCHES AND THEATRES FOR TEN DAYS--PREVALENCE IS GENERAL THROUGHOUT COUNTY--OTHER TOWNS TAKE SIMILAR ACTION  On Monday evening Mayor Hook tabulated the reports of physicians and found 137

---

[19]"Organize to Help Bohemia, People of Spillville Take on New War Work, Will Aid Czechs to Obtain Their Liberty and Take Their Right Place in the World," *The Decorah Republican*, 22 Aug. 1918, n.p., n.c.

[20]"_____," *The Decorah Republican*, 16 Sept. 1918, n.p., n.c.

families represented in the list. . . . At Luther College
between forty and fifty cases were reported. . . .[21]

## Sunday, November 3, 1918

So many dying with the flu. The people who carry out the
dead are carried out themselves the next week. Somebody has
to do it.

Maybe it's a good thing we don't go anywhere. I wish the
boys didn't even have go to town. If they brought home flu to
Johnny he wouldn't have a chance. We'd never forgive
ourselves.

## Monday, November 11, 1918

Such a time as they had in Spillville last night. Joe and
Frank came back from town and said people danced in the
streets and a hastily assembled band played.

> *The Decorah Republican*
> A celebration was held in the [Spillville] town square
> Monday evening in honor that the war was over. The band
> furnished music for the occasion. Rev. Broz and Fred
> Heuser delivered patriotic speeches.[22]

We had known the surrender must be coming--Austria
had surrendered, Turkey dropped everything. Now maybe
Bohemia can gain its independence.

Earlier this fall, the boys were working over at Elert
Brekke's, building a new room on their house. When they cut
through one wall into the attic they saw a clock. When the
boys came home that night all they could talk about was that
clock. It had been built by Elert's father-in-law, Grandpa
Anderson, a few years before he died in 1909. After
accidentally breaking it in moving, they had stored it in the
attic.

Frank and Joe had all sorts of ideas about how they could
fix that clock, so Elert let them bring it home to work on it.
Elert said it was called a "Chimes of Normandy Clock," but it

---

[21]"In the Grip of Influenza," *The Decorah Republican*, 17 Oct. 1918,
n.p., n.c.

[22]"_____," *The Decorah Republican*, 14 Nov. 1918, n.p., n.c.

never played chimes. He wanted it to play music so Joe sent off to one of his magazines and got a music box for it. It has lacey scrollwork on it, like a doily carved in cherry wood. Frank repaired the broken towers and Joe figured out how to restructure the inside to accommodate the music box. The boys could hardly finish supper each night before they had to go tinker with that clock.

Now, two weeks later, the clock runs and keeps time. The boys are excited. Johnny lies on his blanket and watches the pendulum going back and forth. He even tried to clap his hands when the music went off at the hour.

Joe said, "Frank, we could build a clock like this, put a Seth Thomas works in it and the same kind of music box we got for Brekke's."

Frank said, "Let's do." Then he turned to Johnny and said, "Let's do it." And Johnny roared his approval, grinning from ear to ear.

### Wednesday, November 20, 1918

John says there is much talk in Spillville about the big national meeting of Czechs, Slovaks and others in Prague. Thanks to President Wilson's support there may be a new state for Bohemians. Masaryk was chosen as president at the National Assembly.

### Thursday, December 19, 1918

Tonight we celebrated Johnny's thirty-ninth birthday with Brekke's music clock. Life was not the same after Brekke's clock came here and tomorrow it's going back to Brekke's in time for Christmas. But that clock leaves behind an idea, music in the clocks. Johnny would watch that minute hand getting closer and closer to twelve. He was almost breathless with anticipation until the hour struck. Then he'd shout along with the music and wave his arms like he was dancing.

### March 1919

The boys are cleaning out the barn this morning. And all the smells sealed up in the frozen manure piles of winter are released. With trip after trip the greys pull the manure spreader across the fields to help this year's crops. Most people assume these are bad smells, but today I am reminded of the odor of fresh-turned earth. We usually have manure on the garden when Joe or Frank plow it up for me. Anyway, I like to follow the plow out in the fields and used to do so when I was free to walk far away from the house.

### November 1919

Today the boys showed me a small package of the rare holly wood that Mr. Libbey brought to the mailbox. Its whiteness almost has a heavenly glow about it, like the whiteness that must have come from the Star of Bethlehem. And how much I love the smell of holly. Joe and Frank will use it on the face of a clock they are building.

### Friday, December 19, 1919

Johnny's fortieth birthday. It hardly seems a year since we celebrated his thirty-ninth and he had such a good time with that clock. Now he has his own "Chimes of Normandy" on the shelf in the bedroom.

# 6.
# Major Clocks, Crowds
## *1920-1929*

**Sunday, February 29, 1920**

L eap Day!

**Monday, July 19, 1920**

Little Helen Maroushek came today. She likes to hunt gophers in the pasture. Doesn't say much, but I think she likes to watch the boys when they are working on the clocks. But they don't do much with the clocks in summer. Frank was out discing stubble with the Percherons, Nig and Nel, the big black gelding and the dappled gray.

**Sunday, September 5, 1920**

Joseph, dear Joseph, marks forty years today. What a blessing he has been to me through the years! A planner and designer. Frank chuckles and calls him a "schemer." A half-truth there. Joe thinks of the ideas and draws the plans.

I remember how happy I felt when I saw that Joe could crawl, and then when he climbed the furniture. Johnny

**61**

watched him with awe. He seemed to be cheering his brother
on to do what he couldn't do.

Joe and Frank have been out picking some of the earlier
corn. The mornings are cool. The smell of burning weeds
hangs in the air. They come in at noon and night with
sandburs stuck in their socks.

A moment ago I could see Joe cutting the panels for the
"Grand Tower Clock." That will be a magnificent thing if
they ever get it done. We carry out the sawdust by the
bucketsful, which this fall will go on my roses.

### Friday, September 10, 1920

My sixty-third. The boys are picking corn. Mr. Libbey
brought two birthday cards. Why do I cry when I receive mail
like that? Johnny saw me crying and tried to lean out of his
wheelchair to comfort me. Oh, Johnny! I don't know what I'd
do without him. I suppose M. O. Libbey has seen a lot of people
cry--mostly when they don't get mail. That's a better reason.

### Sunday, December 19, 1920

We had Johnny's favorite tapioca pudding tonight.

We have much to be thankful for at the end of this year.
War seems to be behind us. The new Czecho-Slovak state has
a constitution and the governments of the world give
recognition.

### Thursday, January 21, 1921

Today Mr. Libbey brought a big package of wood down the
long driveway. He said he didn't want the package to get wet.
The boys have taken on something they may never get to
finish--the "Apostles' Parade Clock." The twelve apostles
will march around a track every hour, coming out a little
doorway and going on into another.

But that isn't the worst of it. This clock will stand way up
high and look like a cathedral. This plan they sent for
through the mail, but they have added to it. Joe figures he has
pedaled miles of sawcuts with his little scroll saw. If he ever
gets this done, he says, he's never going to do another one.

### Tuesday, January 24, 1922

The air seems to have come down here straight from the North Pole. Close to fifty below zero north of here they say. No cars start in weather like this but Klimesh's and the mailman's. And even Mr. Libbey can't get his going sometimes. The boys jack up the back wheel of the Model T but it's no use. The boys put out extra feed for the cattle.

The cows' teats get frostbitten and then the skin cracks. The cows have painful sores, then kick and knock the bucket over when the boys try to milk them. The boys are trying out a blue salve they have used for saddle sores on the horses.

### Sunday, April 16, 1922

The boys have finished the "Apostles' Parade Clock" and have it running. The boys raced to get it finished by Anna's birthday. The apostles make me think of little old men when they come out every hour and jog along the track. The boys say they got the idea from Father Bily's Corpus Christi celebrations when they saw the children's procession. But there are big old clocks in Bohemia and Switzerland that have moving figures. The boys do like the processions. Not all the priests since Father Bily have liked those celebrations, but the processions surely did have an influence on our children.

The clock gives me a thrill every time I look at it. I don't know how to explain it, but the woodwork looks almost like cloth from a distance, like lace draped from high steeples.

### Monday, January 1, 1923

Joe showed us his plans for a new clock which will be over nine feet tall. I told them they are just going to have to move their clocks out into the barn. Tourists crowd through the parlor so close they sometimes break off little pieces. Something needs to be done before summertime when the crowds come.

This new clock, Joe says, isn't going to have little pieces to break off. He showed me some of the panels which will be built together into a tall cabinet. Each panel, the size of a slice of bread, will have a picture carved into it. The crown molding will be from three different styles--Egyptian, Greek and Roman. 'Twill be a wonderful big clock, but what will become of us? We're being pushed out of our house by clocks--and visitors. People we don't even know stop to see what the boys have done.

The boys are happiest when they are building and carving.

### Sunday, January 21, 1923

This morning I awakened with the smell of fresh coffee cooking. Joe had risen early--said he couldn't sleep, thinking about the design of that "American Pioneer History Clock." Then he remembered it was our anniversary. Funny I didn't hear the sound of the coffee grinder. Nothing raises my hunger and eagerness to get up like the smell of freshly grinding coffee or the smell of it boiling early in the morning.

John and I have been married forty-four years today. And to think! We have four grown children at home yet. Joe building the fire and starting coffee came close to the service I hear about in those big hotels where they serve people breakfast in bed.

### Friday, January 26, 1923

The boys are working steadily on the "American Pioneer History Clock," talking about plans and which scenes from American history to include. They pore over the school books and look at pictures. It will be a good division of labor for them: Joe will do the cabinet work and Frank will carve the panels.

### Friday, February 29, 1924

Here is our extra day, our good luck day. On the other hand, it seems winter lasts longer because we are still in February. I'm sure the daffodils don't know that and they will be coming along by their own calendar.

### Friday, July 4, 1924

Joe and Frank have been cultivating corn, the last time around.

I've canned beans.

Parade in town. We won't go.

**Wednesday, October 1, 1924**

When the boys came in at noon from picking corn I had baked rice pudding--one of Frank's favorites--a little recognition for his fortieth birthday. We'll have chocolate cake tonight.

He said, "Forty years! It's all downhill from here." I told him it wasn't so bad, we're long past forty and look at us! He said, "I have." And then he laughed.

He loves to tease. He tries to act like he's not sentimental, but he's all soft in the heart.

**Monday, January 19, 1925**

Charles and Barbara's golden wedding anniversary. It doesn't seem that long ago we saw them married. And now they've had ten children--four of them married, two of them teachers and Sisters in the Church. The name of Charles Andera has spread around the country for his grave monuments and here at home for his buildings and furniture. Our boys are proud of their cousin, I think, but they never would spend much time to learn from him. Joe would have, if Frank had gone along with him. Our boys have had their farming and their carving.

**October 1925**

A gentle rain last night and the fall leaves smell rich with rotting. They are turning back to soil as we all will some day. Before long everything will be frozen so it's good to have the rain sink in while it still can.

**Sunday, December 27, 1925**

People came all day. John's seventieth birthday. He says he doesn't feel a day over forty.

Our parlor bulges at the seams with clocks. We pulled the other furniture out into the middle of the room so we could put clocks around the walls. Now we have clocks back to back in the middle of the room and some of the furniture out in the barn. We don't have enough wall space. If you put clocks in front of the windows then it makes the room too dark and you can't see the clocks anyway.

Something has to be done. The article in the *Christian Science Monitor* has brought telephone calls from other states.[23]

The boys promise me they will build a display room out in the yard.

**Friday, April 16, 1926**
Anna makes a pretty thirty-nine-year-old. She got out one of her old dress-up dresses and walked around the parlor. Yes, we do have a parlor again! The boys built a display room at last. This morning three of our guineas were sitting on the roof.

Now that the boys have more room, they have started talking about building a miniature of Saint Anthony's Chapel. That chapel has fascinated them for years, ever since we made a trip to Festina in the Model T. It's built where the first Mass was celebrated west of the Mississippi River. And we have a family tie. One of the Gaertners from the family that built the chapel married an Andera.

Now Joe thinks there's room to build a one-inch-to-the-foot replica of Saint Anthony's in their new shop.

**Saturday, April 16, 1927**
Anna's fortieth birthday! I don't think she looks a day over thirty. She went upstairs and put on one of her dressy dresses from when she was twenty. It was a little snug but still wearable. She thinks she looks awful. I say she's too shy, like her mother. She needs to get out more.

We had a good time baking today and lit candles at supper.

Johnny managed to get it out that he was forty and he's O.K. Good American word! O.K.

**Sunday, May 22, 1927**
The boys have been so excited about Lindbergh's flight to Paris this week. They've followed the papers and yesterday went up to the saloon where they were following the flight on radio.

---

[23]The author has not been able to locate this article, although it is frequently mentioned in articles about the Bilys.

**Saturday, September 10, 1927**

My turn to be seventy. The children couldn't be nicer to me.

The boys are talking about building a glass-walled cabinet to hold all their statues. Up to now they've been sitting on dressers and shelves and packed away in boxes.

Frank has been carving a bust of Charles Lindbergh out of a piece of Florida grapefruit wood he ordered out of a catalog. It's beginning to look like the picture of Lindbergh already.

**October 1927**

I stepped into the shop today, the smell of new wood came round me. I do miss the smell of freshly-cut woods since they took their shop out of the house.

They also showed me grapefruit wood which has a citrus smell, and has a whiteness like the first cut of grapefruit rind.

**Saturday, October 29, 1927**

The boys, back from town, told about the two women going over an embankment down near Eldorado. Their Essex dropped into two feet of water, but they got out all right. The women were hunting bittersweet.

They call that matrimony vine around here. There are pretty reddish berries--deadly, though, if a child swallowed them.

**Sunday, November 6, 1927**

The [Decorah] *Journal* says that 296 draft horses were shipped from Decorah this year. I can believe it. The Brekke's have such pretty Morgans--Colonel and Nel. But I especially like Roxy and Ginger with their arched necks and curly manes. Of course our Nig stands bigger and has a shining black coat. Wish we had another just like him.

But now they're talking about tractors. Joe said Mr. Libbey laughed about carrying mail with a tractor. He says horses are easier to start in the morning.

**Saturday, December 10, 1927**

People are still talking about the Forty Hours Devotions held at Saint Wenceslaus last week. There were forty flower girls, with twenty wearing communion veils.

The men are all talking about the new Model A's. Windle Motors up in Decorah said they had a thousand visitors. Of course, if we ever bought one it would be from Charlie Klimesh in Spillville. He's our Ford man.

**Monday, December 19, 1927**
Johnny's forty-eighth birthday!
The player-organ to go into the little Saint Anthony's Chapel came last week, so Joe and Frank hooked it up to play for Johnny tonight. Johnny choked up he was so happy. He doesn't show that much emotion very often, but playing this organ music touched his heart.
Joe says they should make a carving of Babe Ruth. This was a record year with sixty home runs.

**Saturday, January 21, 1928**
Next year will be our golden wedding if we live that long. We were quiet today. Anna made supper for us.
Frank finished carving Charles Lindbergh. Now, where to put it? It shows Lindbergh with his flier's cap and goggles up on his forehead. But Joe says he needs a setting for it, so Joe designed a stylized airplane to be carved out of walnut. It will be a contrast between the white wood of the pilot's face and the dark wood of the machine.
I told Frank he should paint the airplane silver like the "Spirit of St. Louis," but he gave me such a dark look I took a couple of steps backward. He said, "Nothing goes on our wood except vegetable oil."
He and Joe have stubborn ideas about how to treat wood.

**Wednesday, February 29, 1928**
Leap Day!

**Monday, April 16, 1928**
Anna's forty-first birthday--the years seem to fly away. Joe and Frank took Anna and Johnny and me out to the exhibit building to show off their newly completed Saint Anthony's Chapel. It stands along the wall with the clocks and thrusts out into the room more than the other pieces, but the protective railing was planned for that. We had worried about taking the player-organ out of the house because Johnny has listened to it so much. But Johnny knew it had been ordered to be placed

in the chapel. When we offered to leave it in the house and get another one, he made all sorts of motions to say it was to go to the exhibit building. When we offered again to keep it he frowned and swung his arms as if sweeping it out of the house. We will wheel him out there from time to time.

The boys and Anna finally reached an agreement on something they've discussed for months: Should they charge admission? Anna must overcome her shyness about facing strangers. I can't leave the house without Johnny. The boys need to be with their clocks. Joe generally stays in the workshop addition on the east side of the display room and Frank talks to the people as they come through. The boys have now agreed on a dime apiece charge and Anna has agreed to stand outside and do the collecting. It will be good for her, I think, to meet people. She doesn't get *out* enough.

*Mason City Globe-Gazette*
BROTHERS CARVE UNUSUAL CLOCK  Ridgeway-- The most unusual and interesting timepiece, made entirely by hand, to be found in Iowa, and possibly in the United States is at Ridgeway, Winneshiek County, and is the work of two brothers, F. L. and Joseph Bily, farmers. This clock stands eight feet, eight inches high, is four feet, six inches wide, and weighs 500 pounds. It is made up of a series of panels, each panel hand carved in pictorial representations of pioneer scenes.

The clock is called the American Pioneer History Clock, and is the result of four winters of work by the Bily brothers. The design of the clock and the drawing of the various designs for the panels and the joining are all the work of Joseph Bily, while all of the carving is the work of F. L. Bily. Neither of these men (has) had any more than an ordinary grade school education and neither has had any instruction in art or art principles.

Other timepieces which have been made by them follow the old country style of cathedral clock, with much gingerbread scroll saw work, hand-carved figures of the 12 apostles, and some hand carved panels. They are interested, too, in carving small statuettes of Madonnas, the Christ, and Lincoln.

F. L. and Joseph Bily are farmers and have lived for a long time on the farm at Ridgeway. The hands that guided a plow during the day time, that husked hundreds of bushels of corn in the autumn and that daily do the regular chores on a large farm are the same ones which day after day during the winter time guided a pencil on wood or paper and the same that held the tiny chisels and carved a work as smooth as satin.[24]

### Sunday, September 2, 1928

That front page advertisement about the boys, "Have you a Jack Knife?" seemed to bring out people all the more. My! The crowds we had here today! At least Frank got them to put those advertisements off until the end of the season. Of course, it was that *Christian Science* article that brought people in from other states.

They line up in the driveway. Some come to the door and want water from the windmill. Joe usually helps them as I need to stay with Johnny. Anna stands out there with her bucket of dimes and meets everybody. I don't know if she'll ever get used to meeting strangers. She comes in tired in the late afternoon after the last people go home. I couldn't stand out there through the long hot hours. Our notebooks show that over ten thousand people have seen the clocks.

### Monday, September 10, 1928

My seventy-first. The smell of burning Canadian thistles hangs in the air.

### Monday, October 1, 1928

We had a birthday supper for Frank's forty-fourth. He heard this weekend they have built ornamental steps up to the ice cave entrance because there are so many visitors. Everyone has a car anymore and can go fifty miles from home at the drop of a hat. That's why we have so many visitors to see the clocks. He said they have painted DECORAH in great big letters on the roof of Windle's Ford.

### Wednesday, December 19, 1928

Tonight we had tapioca pudding for Johnny's forty-ninth birthday. He makes a great noise over that. When I told how many eggs went into the pudding, Frank pointed to an item in the paper today about a Rhode Island hen that laid 332 eggs in a single year. Joe wondered how many gallon buckets of eggs

---

[24]"Brothers Carve Unusual Clock," *Mason City Globe Gazette*, 28 May 1928, n.p., n.c.

that would be so we had to figure it up. We got all the buckets we could find, put them in a row around the kitchen table and Johnny got a kick out of that. We figured it would take the whole table full of buckets. One chicken did that?

**Sunday, January 20, 1929**
Today we celebrated our golden wedding anniversary, which will actually be tomorrow. A half a century ago we stood with Barbara Bily and John Poshusta at the altar. Frank Kuboushek was here, John's brother Frank and his wife and boys were here and others. It was a nice enough day we got a picture taken at noon out in front of the house.

The Kuboosheks brought a picture of the Little Brown Church we've heard so much about. Joe studied the picture, turned it over in his hands as if he could see the backside of it by turning it around, and then he said, "We can build this. It will go along with Saint Anthony's Chapel."

**Sunday, February 3, 1929**
M. O. Libbey has retired from carrying mail. Twelve years and eight months, they said. And that would about figure out because he came over from Route 1 in May of 1916. Frank laughed about that old car he had--you could hear it all the way out from Ridgeway. We will miss him.

**Tuesday, April 16, 1929**
Anna's forty-second birthday.

The boys run from one thing to another. At night if they're not working on something they read their *Popular Mechanics,* or *National Geographic* or *The American Magazine.* Frank finished up the detail work on the Westminster Abbey base for the "Chimes of Normandy Clock." Joe bends over his drawing table in his shop, working on the framework for the "Little Brown Church." He's having to do it on a scale of one-half inch to the foot where the Saint Anthony model could be an inch to the foot.

I'm glad to see the "Normandy Clock" up on a high base which will keep the clock away from the prying fingers of little children. A few mothers will let their children climb around behind the rail and go exploring the clocks. Frank gently lifts them back over the rail, back into their mother's arms, and goes on with his tour.

**Sunday, June 16, 1929**
The boys got a copy of *The American Art Student and Commercial Artist*. It has advertised sculpture photos which they want to study for making carvings.

**Monday, June 17, 1929**
Frank brought home a clipping one of the Klimesh boys gave him. It was from the St. Paul Sunday paper. It said, "Some haughty-looking guinea hens step about in front of the sheet iron structure which, standing between the roadway and the farm house, serves as an exhibition room for the fifteen or sixteen clocks on display . . . the Bilys learned last summer to compensate themselves for the time consumed in attending to the visitors. . . . Their system now is to charge a small entrance fee."[25]

**Monday, September 30, 1929**
Cousin Charles Andera's funeral today had people from three states. He died last Friday. Take away what he has done for Spillville and for cemeteries across the country, and what a lot of vacant places there would be. It seems strange to think that he will never again be in his carpenter's shop there by the church. Who will make a monument for him?
Dear Charlie, I will always be thankful for the encouragement you gave to our boys. Not that they went to see you that much, but every time they saw you at work carving a form, they seemed to remember every little thing you said and did.

**Thursday, December 19, 1929**
Oh, Johnny! Fifty years--can it be that long? Fifty years of waiting for others to meet your needs, of lying on your blanket, of sitting in your chair. Please, God, forgive me for those times I have felt locked in. I could not have been locked in with a more gracious and patient friend.
We celebrated with tapioca pudding. Joe told how it's called cassava in South America and has a poison in it at first. It's related to the Indian soap weed they have out on the prairies.

25"_____," *Pioneer Press*, 16 Jun. 1929, n.p., n.c.

# 7.
# Clock Building, Clock Showing, Death of Johnny
## *1930-1939*

Tuesday, January 21, 1930

O ur fifty-first anniversary.

Wednesday, January 22, 1930

The cold creeps in everywhere like icy tentacles. The water freezes in the dishpan. It seems we do little else than carry out ashes and lug in more wood. Trees pop like gunshots. Over thirty below zero. We have to gather the eggs at noon to keep them from freezing.

Wednesday, April 16, 1930

I put a cake in the oven while Anna was out doing chicken chores. Surprised her. She thought I had built up the fire to take the chill off, but then she smelled the cake baking.

**73**

**July 1930**

The cars were lined up in the driveway again this Sunday. Some leave their engines running and the southeast wind carries the smell through the house. Tonight I keep thinking that a lamp wick was turned up too far and smoked the chimney, but, no, what we have is a little remembrance of the cars idling in the driveway most of the day.

**Friday, September 5, 1930**

Joe worked in the shop all day on his fiftieth birthday. He'd rather do that than anything. This time of year they used to be out in the cornfields. Now the neighbors do it.

**Thursday, December 25, 1930**

The boys are working on the old Swedish clock that a man brought in this year. He said it's over 250 years old--a lovely, leafy old thing, but awfully banged up. I think it had been dropped, or played with. Now with the boys' additions and refinishing it could go in any museum. Frank said, "We purposely left our carving a little rough so you could tell what we added and what was the original work." But it doesn't look rough to me and I think the proportions are better now. This one stays in the house, for awhile anyway.

This year the boys have nearly finished the statuary clock. They've gathered up heads from all over the house to put in it. The people who come to visit the display room this summer can see the boys' work going back thirty years.

**Wednesday, April 8, 1931**

The *Decorah Journal* today had an explanation for that roaring we heard in the sky the other night. John had said he thought it was an airplane. The moon shone through the clouds but not enough for an airplane to land safely. But, it was an airplane, the paper said.

New Model A Fords are for sale for $430, but few people have the money.

*Mason City Globe Gazette*
THRONGS ATTRACTED TO CLOCK COLLECTION OF BILY BROTHERS ON RIDGEWAY FARM: IOWA ARTISTS' FAME SPREADS THRUOUT NATION; MUCH WORK REPRESENTED, by Phil Lamar Anderson

Ridgeway, June 11  Time hung heavy for two Iowa farmers after completion of their daily work in the fields.

And therein lies an unusual story--a story about the Bily brothers of near Ridgeway, and a score of artistically hand carved clocks of many kinds of wood, which they have designed and produced. . . .

Until a few years ago, no one aside from neighbors of the Bily brothers had ever heard of their farm home guest parlor that was crowded with hand carved clocks of all types and descriptions. For 20 years Joe, who is 45, and Frank, four years younger, had been adding section by section to clocks of the tall, hall-room variety and one by one their works of art were completed and set beside a wall or in a corner.

The clocks stood side by side, each telling the same time of day, each measuring a steady tick-tock, tick-tock, tick-tock, each indicating another new creation. . . .

Today . . . the two farmers have their clocks on display in a narrow building, 50 feet in length. . . .

To this rural museum last year went 19,000 visitors from all parts of the nation--and a few foreign countries as well--each of whom was eager to pay the dime admission the Bily brothers apologetically collect for a view. . . .

Modestly, Joe and Frank Bily have little to say about themselves. They act as guides when persons come to their "museum" and willingly volunteer explanations about the kinds of wood . . . the mechanical features . . . the music boxes imported either from Sweden or . . this country.

The Bilys, as boys, used to do considerable whittling and carving when in and out of their school room.  Their jackknives were always handy. . . . Desks frequently came under their sharp blades and outlines of hearts with arrows pointing inwardly were common creations of the carvers. Yet, ironically enough, neither Joe nor Frank ever married the girls for whom they did their boyhood mischievousness and received spankings from teachers as due punishment; both are bachelors now. . . .

Their visitors have included world-famed art collectors who have offered thousands of dollars just for removal of a single clock from the exhibit. One collector handed the Bily brothers a check for $16,000. . . . They turned it down. In view of such offers, the galaxy of time pieces is valued around $25,000 to $30,000 by wood carving authorities.

. . . They have rented their 120 acres of land, and devote their days to greeting visitors who come to see their clocks. At night their carving activities still go on.

Perhaps the device that causes the greatest amount of comment from sightseers is one known as the Apostles clock. This, incidentally, was the first clock the Bily brothers constructed which carried carving. It was built in 1915 and 1916, and improved in 1917.

### SHOWS SPILLVILE CHURCH

The base of this clock has a carved representation of the Town Hall of Prague, Bohemia, in front; on one side is shown the Charles bridge and tower in the same city, and on the other side is shown the Catholic church in Spillville. . . .

Once each hour, [through] the controls of a mechanism, the figures of the dozen apostles parade in front of the clock. Each of these figures was carved from boxwood with a penknife, the Bilys explained. The figures are lifelike; each is in a different standing pose. Were one to cut the figures from a photograph they could not appear more realistic. As they slowly move, the visitor in the Bily exhibit hall senses an air of sacredness about this work of art. When the hour is near, the spectators become quiet. One can hear a pin drop, so tense is the crowd.

Music is produced within the clock. It is characteristic of that heard in church music, soft and melodious. Then the apostles commence their march. One by one their procession is augmented until eventually all 12 apostles are to be seen in a line. The music continues. The hour is struck on chimes within the clock. The apostles continue moving. One by one they pass inside a door and disappear. Soon all are out of sight. The music ceases.

### VISITORS PRAISE BILYS

During this exhibition, the crowd has stood wide-eyed and breathless. The apostles' parade has been brief, but attention-compelling.

Visitors turn, one to another. The exhibit building becomes noisier. There is talking, the moving of feet as persons move on to view another clock. Above it all, however, comment is heard, words of praise for the Bily brothers, phrases of amazement at what has been witnessed; declarations about the Apostle clock, indicating it alone is worth traveling miles to gaze upon, to study, to see in operation.

.............................................................

The Bily brothers' cathedral type clocks follow the best designs obtainable for such creations--clocks made centuries ago in European countries. Some of the designs, of course, have been improved by the Iowa carvers.

Four of the cathedral type clocks have become outstanding in the amount of handiwork that each has entailed in its production and perfection, as anyone can see at a glance. One, known as the Grand Tower clock, is of hard maple. The hands and figures are of ebony. The dial is of white hollywood. The base is black walnut. It has cuckoo clock works and a set of Swiss chimes. Another is a Roman Renaissance clock, which resembles the capitol style of architecture which originated hundreds of years ago in Italy. Hard maple was used in this for the most part. The base is of ash and birchwood.

## HEAR SWISS CHIMES

Every half hour the door below the clock dial opens and a tiny figure of George Washington, hand carved from boxwood, appears while imported Swiss chimes play either "Home Sweet Home" or "My Old Kentucky Home." Still a third clock is known as the Chimes of Normandy, a creation representing the Norman architectural work and styles of ornamentation used in the "old country," as the Bilys explained it. It is of black walnut.

The fourth of this series of clocks is "just a hall clock," as the Bilys said, which they made from selected European cherry wood. When the clock strikes on the half hour, a door automatically opens and three figures representing a village band appear in the entrance way as a tune is played on a hidden music box. The Bilys said they made these four clocks years ago, when they first started to carve.

## BILYS ORIGINATE CLOCKS

Not only have the Bily brothers been emulators of architectural splendors of European capitals; they have been originators as well. Their first original clock depicts in artistic carvings [a] history of American pioneer days. They refer to it as their most ambitious piece of carving. It is, by the way, one of three clock designs originated by them. This clock, which required spare time--between 1923 and 1927, is made of cherry and walnut woods. It stands eight feet, eight inches high, is four feet and six inches wide, and weighs more than 500 pounds.

The clock design is a series of panels representing scenes in American history. Many of the scenes have been copied from famous works of art, but many more are original with the makers. The top of the clock is finished with beautiful carvings of classic border designs. One highest in the clock is a design from the Temple of Jupiter. Another is the carving from a Greek pattern. Adjacent is work from a Roman pattern. The base border panels show a forest with medalions of Indians' heads. Border designs illustrate the methods of log cabin construction.

FOUR AGES OF LIFE APPEAR

American made chimes have been installed in this clock. While they play "America" the four ages of life--childhood, youth, middle age and old age--parade forth from concealment in a space behind a panel whose carving depicts the Mayflower, remain in view until the song has been played and automatically disappear from sight.

Some idea of what has been accomplished in the four years of carving on just this one clock may be gained from a study of the titles of the scenes. Each panel in the clock is unique in itself. There is depicted a Zuni Indian village, the battle of Tippecanoe, a life-like Indian holding a peace pipe, a view of the Liberty Bell, detachable figures of the American soldier, American sailor, LaFayette; a conception of the Statue of Liberty and another of Abraham Lincoln splitting rails.

But those are not all. Still another row of carvings around the clock reveal a scene of frontier settlers on a homestead while the ceiling of the same panel depicts some of the pioneer day tools that were in use. There is a view of John Hancock, Thomas Jefferson and Benjamin Franklin signing the Declaration of Independence. Betsy Ross is shown making a flag. Chief Black Hawk is included in the carvings, and the seal of the United States has not been overlooked. On the clock's face is a study called "The Fairy of the Moon," and above it eagles flying, while below are shown elk and deer.

To the average reader, the aforementioned carvings would seem to be sufficient to take two men four years to complete. There is still more to be seen on this historical clock, however.

CARVINGS ON FOUR SIDES

When one considers that this clock is not just an exhibit on which the dexterity of the Bily brothers is shown on one, or the front side, but is equally artistic on all sides, it is not difficult to appreciate these added scenes in the various panels:

Washington sworn in as president; the Mayflower, cowboys, Chief Sitting Bull, Kit Carson and his favorite horse, Apache; Sacajawea pointing Lewis and Clark to the Pacific Ocean; studies of General Sam Houston, David Crockett, Daniel Boone; a pioneer woman weaving; the first locomotive in the United States; the Spirit of '76; an Indian war dance, and an Indian woman with a papoose on her back.

Still other panels show the landing of the Pilgrims, a group of old pioneers, family of pioneers building a home, emigrants moving westward with covered wagons, a grouping of Captain Crawford, Seth Paxson and a Kiowa Indian, an Indian tepee, breaking sod with ox team and wooden plow, scene of the sower, and primitive natives hunting buffalo.

These are but the highlights of the carvings which attract the most attention of visitors to the Bily farm. Others, equally as historic, intersperse those that have been mentioned. It cannot be unappreciated, this claim of the Bilys, that their American pioneer history clock is their most ambitious work to date; to see it is not to doubt their statement that it represents years of conscientious labor.

There is, in the exhibit, another which is known as the Apostles' Parade clock. It was constructed by the Bilys during the years 1921 and 1922; was the largest clock and carried the largest amount of hand carving of any pieces of work that they had done up to that time. It is eight feet, nine inches high, and is carved mainly from walnut, rosewood, hard maple and cherry woods. As in the Apostles' clock, there are 12 miniature wooden Apostle figures which parade every hour in this creation. Each was carved from basswood. As the clock's set of chimes are heard on the hour, the apostles pass in parade inside the clock, a small door being automatically opened just before the first figure comes into view and immediately closed when the twelfth apostle has filed by.

CARVING CLOCK WORKS NOW

The Bilys also have in the course of construction a hall clock which has carved wooden works. They explained that the wheels, shafts, plates, dial hands, and figures all are made of wood with the exception of the cogs of one wheel, the escapement, these being metal points set on a wooden wheel. This clock, when completed will have an automatic calendar, the figures on the dial being inlaid in the clock face.

While this story is chiefly about clocks, the statuary work done by the Bily brothers cannot be omitted. And, true to form, the statues made by these prolific carvers are exhibited in a glass-encased clock of the hall type for inspection from three sides. This statuary clock was made during the past three years, 1928-30. It stands nine feet, six inches high, and is carved mainly in black walnut, oak and boxwood. On its base is carved a representation of the west

front of Iowa's old capitol building at Iowa City; on the right
end appears a carving of the barracks of old Fort Atkinson
which is only a short distance from carved representation of
the oldest church in the United States, the San Miguel chapel
at Santa Fe, New Mexico, the Bilys explained. Inside the
glass are to be seen the busts and full-figure statues of
Shakespeare, Wagner and Dvořák; Mrs. William Day, first
white settler at Decorah, Abraham Lincoln, Ulysses S. Grant,
Masaryk, the first president of Czecho-Slovakia, and others.

But most interesting of all are the three figures
depicting musicians whose arms are moved by hidden
mechanism and the players keep perfect time to the tuneful
music-box rendition. Not content with these
accomplishments, the Bily brothers added two statuary
figures to the top of the clock, one representing Day; the
other Night. It might be explained that sculpture in wood is
regarded as the most difficult form of wood carving. Yet the
Bilys, their visitors exclaim, have mastery over all![26]

### Friday, July 31, 1931

My! This has been a hot month. Several days around one
hundred degrees or over. My garden has wilted.

[Tucked in between pages lay an old, torn, yellowed
newpaper clipping. Here is part of it.]

*The Decorah Journal*
. . . true version of wedding that occured last week, the
article our editor refused to publish because it told the truth.
It reads:
"LIMP CHILTING GETS BUMPED OFF. Benjamin
Chilting, alias 'Limp' and Esmaralda Baxter were married at
twilight-fall at the home of the bride's parents, Rev. Jet
Benson, officiating.
"The groom is a popular young bum who hasn't done a
lick of work since he was kicked out of Will Jenkins' Drug
Store for juggling intimately with the cash register. He
manages to dress well and keep a supply of spending money
because his dad is a soft-hearted old fool who takes up his
bad checks instead of letting him go to jail where he belongs.

---

[26]Phil Lamar Anderson, "Throngs Attracted to Clock Collection of
Bily Brothers on Ridgeway Farm," *Mason City Globe-Gazette*, 11 June
1931, n.p., n.c.

"The popular bride is a skinny fast little devil who has been kissed by every boy in town since she was 12 years old. She paints like an Obijah Indian, sucks cigrettes in secret, and has a surprising capacity for mean corn liquor when she is out joyriding in her dad's Model T at night. She doesn't know a thing about cooking, sewing or keeping house decent.

"The house was freshly plastered for the wedding and the exterior newly painted, to carry out appropriately the decorative scheme, for the groom was newly plastered also, and the bride's exterior was newly painted. The groom wore a rented dinner suit over athletic underwear of imitation silk. His trousers were held up by pale green suspenders. His number 8 patent leather shoes matched his state of tightness and harmonized nicely with the axle grease polish of his hair. In addition to the jag, he carried a pocket knife, a bunch of keys, a dun for the ring and his usual look of imbecility.

"The Bride wore some kind of white thing that left most of her legs sticking out at one end and her bony upper end sticking out at the other. The young couple will make their home with the bride's parents which means they will sponge on the old man till he dies and then she will take in washing."

Just because I used to be the editor of our home town paper . . . [27]

[the rest is torn off]

### Thursday, September 10, 1931

My seventy-fourth.

Johnny was excited to hear about the carrier pigeon from Moline, Illinois, that stopped in Decorah. It had ribbons attached to its legs with the address. Frank took Johnny out to the barn where they listened to the pigeons and talked about pigeons.

### Saturday, September 12, 1931

Joe took my sponge cakes into the A.B.C.S.[American Brotherhood of Catholic Societies] Hall for the big Saint Wenceslaus benefit tomorrow.

---

[27]R. Lee Sharpe, "Old Time Editor Decides to Write True Wedding Story," *The Decorah Journal*, 26 Aug. 1931, n.p., n.c.

Everybody's talking about picking corn. The boys are planning to help with the neighbors starting Monday.

### Friday, September 18, 1931

Another man attacked by a dairy bull--a Mr. Phillips over toward Ridgeway. Good thing his boys were there to save his life. Pulled the bull away by the rope fastened to the ring in his nose. Frank says that's why we have shorthorns. They're not so mean as those Holsteins. Not so high strung, I guess.

Johnny laughed out loud tonight when Joe read to him about the Gopher Man. That Minnesota man caught over 500 gophers in fifteen days. He opens up the hole to let light in, then sets the trap over the hole. They can't stand light so they come up to mound up the dirt again.

Johnny remembers the day we let him sit in his wheelchair out in the pasture while we went into the nearby trees to cut up wood. Joe told him if he stayed still a long time the gophers would come up. And sure enough, after a long wait he had seen several gophers running from hole to hole.

But he doesn't like to think of them trapped. He laughed to remember them scurrying from hole to hole, but he frowned and shook his head when we said the Gopher Man got ten cents apiece bounty. Johnny knows the meaning of being trapped-- trapped inside a body that won't work right.

### Saturday, September 19, 1931

Joe saw me writing in this diary and asked if I would write down a clipping he's been carrying around. He's afraid he'll lose it. He got it out of the *Journal* a week or so ago.

#### ON THE MAJESTY OF TREES

There is nothing more majestic than a tree, there is nothing which whispers more words of cheer and comfort if one has the ears with which to hear it than a tree. There is nothing that carries with it more grandeur and more stately beauty than a tree. Man may go about the country and build wonderful statues, beautiful buildings, and scenic spots, but in all his ingenuity he can never approach anything like that which God has built in a tree.[28]

---

[28]Ray Lucas, "Ray Lucas Writes a Wholesome Essay on the Majesty of Trees," *The Decorah Journal,* 2 Sept. 1931, n.p., n.c.

There was more, but this was what he wanted written down.

They've found that murdered man. Joe and Frank had gone over to the highway last month to see that three-wheeled Dodge Touring car. It was a funny-looking thing, but not so funny for the man who owned it.

### Thursday, September 24, 1931

Mildred Balik had her appendix taken out. She came home from college and ate too much home cooking, I suppose. Anyway, they could take it out. Wonderful how they can open up the body and close it again. When I was her age, they couldn't have done a thing. "Died of indigestion," they'd say.

They've put new sound machines in the Lyric Theatre. The talkies are the thing now. We'd never get in there with the wheelchair.

Father Dobberstein over at West Bend's Grotto sued that girl who crashed into him in Dubuque. He knows how to go to court since he had trouble with his caged bear.[29]

The boys are actually working on three new clocks, Joe drawing the designs and building the cabinets and Frank carving the details. Joe and Frank got the idea for one clock after a Model T ride around northeast Iowa. When they returned they kept talking about how everywhere they went people were rush, rush, rushing, like they were out of time. So, the first clock, the boys say, represents people's struggle for time. We have so many timesaving devices but people keep saying, "I don't have time." Everyone talks about how poor they are, and yet cars are buzzing everywhere. Any driver who affords a gallon of gas will go to the next town. I suppose I shouldn't complain--that's why they come out here to the farm and bring their dimes.

The second clock will look a little like the "Struggle for Time Clock" in that it rounds out on top like a tree. It will be the "Clock of the Forest." The third rises like a skyscraper-- one for the people of the world. A globe will turn and people of

---

[29]An unattended child visiting the West Bend, Iowa, Grotto of the Redemption was mauled by Father Dobberstein's caged bear. The family sued and Father Dobberstein's defense made national news.

the world in their native costumes will march around. The
boys wrote letters to several countries to get pictures of those
costumes. I wonder if the boys will ever get them all done.

### Saturday, December 19, 1931

The boys came in early from chores and took their
Saturday night baths. They were getting cleaned up for
Johnny's party.

But Johnny seemed so subdued when we tried to help him
celebrate his birthday tonight. I'm worried about him.

He seemed sad when we talked about his fifty-second
birthday. But then, when he saw we were getting sad with
him, he tried to cheer us up. Oh! If only he could get unlocked!
If only he could get out of his cage of flesh. Yet, we don't want
him to leave us.

### Thursday, January 21, 1932

Tonight after supper we sat around and talked--talked
through the fifty-three years since we were married. Talked
of the Old Country. Talked of the ships we came on from
Europe.

Then we talked of when the boys were little, and our little
darling Anna came along. There were only five grades in
the country school when the boys went there. Maybe we should
have insisted they go on to town school. They might have gone
on and made successes in the world. But, no, they said,
everything had worked out just right. They wouldn't change
a thing. And after all, it's not everybody that has had Henry
Ford offer them a million dollars for something they made.
And Anna said, "Maybe we didn't go out in the world, but the
world has come to us with people lining up on our driveway on
summer Sundays."

We were talking along and all of a sudden I saw Johnny
looking at me so strangely, so seriously. I realized then that
he had been quiet for a long time, watching us.

I asked him if something was wrong. He just shook his
head and smiled. He picks up our moods so quickly. But, this
was something else.

### Sunday, February 14, 1932

John said that at Mass, Father Broz talked about Saint
Valentine--the Saint of Love. We Czechs have never talked

much about this Saint of Ireland, but Saint Valentine's Day gets attention across America like Easter or the Fourth of July--a big day in America. The children exchange Valentine greetings in school.

The boys have finished the "Struggle for Time Clock" and are quite along the way with the "Clock of the Forest." They remembered how we talked about the forests of Old Bohemia. They have carved this piece with lots of curved lines, rounded on top like a tree.[30]

### Monday, February 29, 1932

Leap Day.

Tomorrow comes the farmers' moving day. This year, sadly, most farmers who must move, are moving off the farm. We can't get a fair price for grain or livestock. Often cold, raw weather for moving, for driving cattle and carrying furniture on hayracks, the cold must seem worse when one is forced to leave home. But it's the day agreed upon. It comes after the worst of winter and just ahead of planting. Renters moving to a new farm have a chance to start ahead of the growing season. Those going to town hunt for jobs.

Joe and Frank came home tired from helping a neighbor move. But they did chores and went right to the shop. They are excited about their big "Parade of Nations Clock." Foreign embassies have sent pictures of the costumes they need. The earth, a ball almost too big to put one's arms around and hug, will turn each hour. Thirty-six carved figures in costume will turn with it.

### Saturday, April 16, 1932

Tonight we celebrated Anna's forty-fifth birthday. I had made her a bright new apron and a matching bonnet out of a piece of cloth John had brought home.

We have all been upset over the kidnapping of the Lindbergh baby. The boys have brought home the newspapers

---

[30]During 1932, editorials appeared in regional newspapers decrying the cutting down of the virgin forests of Winneshiek County. One authority observed that areas where Czech farmers have control of the land, such as farms around Spillville, the forests have been better preserved. Also of note, the caves of Winneshiek are being explored and a cave does appear in the base of the Bily's "Clock of the Forest."

that tell about it. I think it has affected Johnny. Tonight he seemed subdued again. I'm worried about him. I can see it in his eyes, as if he were looking at us from a long distance.

### Friday, May 6, 1932
Johnny left us. In spite of anything we could do, he slipped away. I could see it in his eyes before he died--as if he were already looking at us from beyond the grave.[31]

### Monday, May 9, 1932
The house seems so empty. Even while Johnny's body lay here it seemed as if I could expect him to call at any moment. Now he's gone away on a trip--alone--something he never did. For fifty-two years, there was always one of us with him. Now he's traveled on ahead of us.

We opened the windows to let him go when he left us. And in came the lilacs and apple blossoms on the breeze.

Never did he call in the night unless he really needed me. He was so sweet and bore any pain quietly. What can he tell us in heaven? Can we talk it all over someday?

Tonight it seems like one of the stars shines more brightly outside my window.

### Friday, May 13, 1932
He has been gone a week. Has ever anything been so hard? I know he's better off. I pray God he has a beautiful body now. But we are so alone. I can't bear to look at his wheelchair.

### Thursday, May 19, 1932
I told John about Joe's name showing up in the newspaper: "Seventy-four dollars and fifty-eight cents dragging the county roads." Oh, how Joe earned that money from the county! He would leave early in the morning, hardly waiting to eat his breakfast, take his team and walk up the driveway

---

[31]John Evangelist died May 6, 1932. Did he get to see the world turn with the "Parade of Nations"? We have reason to believe he was keenly observant. In fact, the insistence by Joe and Frank on having music in the early clocks was partly to please their brother who had to spend long hours alone in his chair and who showed pleasure at the music. They would give him credit for getting them started carving.

and out of sight. Then come home, black with dust. I could
see the tiredness in his eyes. Frank went too, some days, to
give Joe a break. Frank would tease, saying, "I'm still in my
forties. Better let a young man drag the roads." Joe would
roll his eyes at Frank, but wouldn't say a word. The next
morning they'd talk about it over oatmeal to decide which one
would go.

The money helped pay our taxes. We shouldn't have
rented out the land, I suppose.

### Sunday, May 22, 1932

Amelia Earhart Putnam has flown alone across the
Atlantic and beat Charles Lindbergh's record by several
hours. People at Mass were talking about it.

I am supposedly free to go to church now, without Johnny to
care for. But too many years have given me the habit of
staying home. I feel like jumping out of the church pew and
running back to the farm to see about my boy.

### Wednesday, May 25, 1932

Joe Swehla had a close call this week on the Conover Road.

The *Decorah Journal* advertised to the world this week that
I paid my $64.34 in taxes. In this country everybody knows
everything about the neighbors. At least, Joe and Frank
didn't have to work this tax off on the county road.

### Wednesday, July 13, 1932

Joe and Frank went up to Ridgeway to see the new bank.
And this week the cost of mailing a letter goes up from two
cents to three cents. We'll write postcards.

### Saturday, July 30, 1932

The boys have been helping with the oats harvest all week.
Today they went to town. Frank said, "Hogs are up to $1.45.
We should be in the pig business. But, by the time you get
started the prices are down again."

### Saturday, August 6, 1932

Joe and Frank came back from town talking about the
staged train wreck the Iowa State Fair will put on. They're
going to have two big locomotives crash into each other at fifty

miles an hour.  Frank says that's like hitting a stone cliff at a
hundred miles an hour.

I say, "What a waste!"

**Saturday, September 10, 1932**
The boys always used to pick corn at the time of my
birthday.  Joe got his shucking pegs out and looked at them--I
think he feels kind of at a loss with others picking and he
isn't.

The boys have started on another clock, named after a
Quaker woman they read about last winter--Elizabeth Fry.
Frank read her story aloud to Johnny, and of course I heard it
too.  What personal power she had, to face prison officials in
England and France.  She stands out in the boys minds as
truly one of the world's heroines.

**Tuesday, December 27, 1932**
John marked seventy-seven and still going strong!

**Sunday, January 1, 1933**
A quiet day.  We made popcorn, roasting it with the
screenwire basket in the stove.

**Saturday, January 21, 1933**
Our fifty-fourth wedding anniversary.  Our first
anniversary without Johnny.  The house seems so empty
without him.  I'm sorry I cannot write when I think about him.

**Monday, March 6, 1933**
Roosevelt has closed the banks today.  What won't he do
next?  Fortunately we didn't have much in there and what
little we have we'll probably get back.  Czechs play it a little
closer to the belt than some folks.  Czechs don't write checks.
Not as many, anyway.

The boys have finished the "Elizabeth Fry Clock."  Frank
said they only used three tools to carve the whole thing.  Now
they are back at the "Parade of Nations."[32]  They're having a
lot of technical problems with so many moving parts.

---

[32]The "Parade of Nations Clock," reveals the Bily's vision of
international community at a time when America had many isolationist
sentiments. The Bilys were reading widely and listening to Will Rogers on
the radio who jokingly asked how we would feel if China had a gunboat

**Sunday, April 16, 1933**

Anna's birthday--her forty-sixth this year--this was always the time the boys would be going out to plant corn. My birthday came when they were just going out to pick.

The boys have been working on the "Parade of Nations Clock" all winter. Now they must lay the work aside and get ready for the weekend visitors this summer. Thank God most of them come on Sundays. Some will come at other times when we women are here alone. Since we charge that admission a few feel as if they can come any time they have a dime ready. Anna patiently takes them through.

**Saturday, May 6, 1933**

Johnny went to heaven a year ago today. How can anyone understand how two lives can be so intertwined unless they went through what Johnny and I went through. Not a day goes by but I think of him. Often not an hour goes by. I dream of him, I hear him moving about and I am out of bed, only to realize Johnny left a year ago. Dear Johnny, we love you and miss you.

**Wednesday, December 27, 1933**

John celebrates seventy-eight today. He thought he would never live this long.

The states have wiped Prohibition off the slate. John says that's his birthday present and laughs. He does like his beer. The intent of Prohibition was good, but it made criminals out of too many. My boys go in each week for their beer and have a little in the evening while they work. It's too bad many can't handle it that way.

Sixty thousand artists leaving Germany. It reminds me of how they used to take a canary down into the mines. When the canary keeled over it was time to get out. The canary has died in Germany. Bohemia has been free from Austria awhile, but I'm afraid it won't be long before we are overrun by the Germanic race.

---

policy like ours--if the Chinese sent gunboats up the Mississippi to protect their Chinese laundries in Memphis.

**Sunday, January 21, 1934**

Five years since our Golden Wedding and we wondered if we would live that long!

The boys have the "Parade of Nations" up and running. Now they are laying out plans for one they will call the "Paradise Clock." It will have Adam and Eve and the Serpent. Then some of the animals that Frank has been carving through the years will find a place under the trees. They are using white ash instead of holly which they can't get any more. They'll also use butternut and oak that they can get right here at home.

**Monday, April 16, 1934**

Ann at forty-seven thinks she's getting gray. I tell her it looks distinguished.

**Sunday, May 6, 1934**

All day long you have been in my mind, Johnny. I hear the squeak of your chair. I listen for you to call, and then I remember, you are gone. But, sometimes you seem so close. Can it be two years?

**Wednesday, July 14, 1934**

It was so hot today the corn wilted. 115 degrees! There are usually drownings when it gets like this. Holy Mother, watch over our children.

**Monday, October 1, 1934**

We had a cake and one candle Sunday noon for the last day of Frank's forties.

**November 1934**

The pleasant sour smell of silage drifted in the windows this morning. Maybe the sour smell is what I like about sauerkraut. The neighbors had dug a trench and put in the chopped corn. At least they'll have something to feed this winter--and something to smell on winter mornings!

**Monday, May 6, 1935**

Three years today you left us. How you looked for the crocuses and you celebated each tulip come May time. How often I wished I could drag your chair to the farthest end of the garden for you noticed everything that grew.

> *Mason City Globe Gazette*
> Ridgeway--Another masterpiece has been added to the famous collection of the Bily clocks, skillful handwork of Iowa's famous woodworkers, Frank L., and Joseph Bily. The latest work, pictured here, is the Paradise clock. It stands eight feet six inches tall and weighs 400 pounds, being made of butternut, white ash and white oak. The work embodies an unusual conception of the Garden of Eden, including Adam and Eve, the Tree of Life and the serpent. [33]

### Friday, August 16, 1935

Will Rogers and Wiley Post died yesterday up in Alaska. Frank sat at the table for an hour this morning. He acts like they were members of our own family. Will Rogers always said he would die with his boots on and I guess he has. So sad. We needed Will for the sanity of this country.

### Friday, December 27, 1935

John turned eighty today. We will have oyster stew tonight like we used to have to celebrate the end of cornpicking, and for John's birthday. We don't give up those cornpicking traditions easily.

Some folks talked like they might come visit Sunday if the weather is all right.

Frank talked about Milan Hodza, the premier of Czechoslovakia. T. J. Masaryk resigned. A lot happening there we don't know about.

### Tuesday, January 21, 1936

Our fifty-seventh wedding anniversary.

### Saturday, February 29, 1936

We make up a day again. I wonder what it would be like if the earth and the sun came out in their travels so that each year was exactly the same? We would be able to know what

---

[33]"Paradise Clock Made," *Mason City Globe Gazette*, 26 July 1935, n.p., n.c.

day of the week any birthday would be in the future. But, maybe that would be too regular to be interesting.

### Thursday, April 16, 1936

Anna's forty-ninth. She says this is the last year. She will not be fifty. However, she said something like that when she was twenty-nine and thirty-nine. I said, "Why don't you have Joe drive you uptown and buy a new dress." She looked at me like I was out of my mind. Then, when she tired of looking at me, she looked away and said, "Someday, maybe, someday."

I don't know what all that meant.

> *The Decorah Journal*
>
> SCENIC BEAUTIES OF DECORAH AND WINNESHIEK COUNTY TOLD TO EAST BY MRS. BIERMANN IN RADIO TALK: BROADCASTS FINE PUBLICITY FOR AREA IN "HOME TOWN HOUR" ON WASHINGTON STATION
>
> ... Miss Mason (question): Mrs. Biermann, I have been told that there is a marvelous collection of clocks near Decorah. What can you tell me about them?
>
> Mrs. Biermann (answer): The Bily Brothers are Bohemian farmers who live between Spillville and Ridgeway in Winneshiek County. For many years they have devoted their winters to the making of beautiful clocks, hand carved in a great variety of wood. Today these numerous clocks are kept in a building on the Bily farm. Every year thousands of visitors from all parts of the United States come to this farm. Bily Brothers have refused large sums of money for some of their handiwork. The managers of the recent Chicago World's Fair endeavored without success to induce the artistic farmers to exhibit their collection at the World's Fair. The Bily Brothers are content to have their beloved clocks on the farm where they were made and to take as financial reward only ten cents admission.[34]

---

[34]"Scenic Beauties of Decorah and Winneshiek County Told to East by Mrs. Biermann in Radio Talk," *The Decorah Journal*, 11 Mar. 1936, p. 4, cols. 3-4.

**Wednesday, May 6, 1936**

Sometimes I try to picture you in heaven, Johnny, your body whole and healed, but I cannot for long. I see you again as a baby threshing about on the blanket, and then tied up in a chair with rags. Sometimes I see your face, but you still struggle without speech. Was it something we did? Lord have mercy. Christ have mercy.

But you are beautiful through it all. Your love did shine through your brokenness. Four years since you left us.

> *The Decorah Journal*
> SCENERY LAUDED BY MOTOR GROUP: A.A.A. OF IOWA ADVISES . . . Decorah, the scenic and historic crossroads of the Middle West, is located on U. S. Highway No. 52 and Iowa 9; has 125 acres of beautiful parks on the banks of the historic Upper Iowa river. Within a few miles of Decorah are the Bily clocks, the Dvořák Memorial, the Smallest Church, and the State Park at Fort Atkinson.[35]

**Monday, July 6, 1936**

They say, "A cold winter, a hot summer." It's true this year. The thermometer must stay up all night too, though I don't want to light a lamp to see. The sheets stick to our skin. We fan each other with magazines, or walk around. At least Johnny isn't having to suffer with us.

**Monday, July 13, 1936**

Another day and a night when we couldn't sleep. When it gets over a hundred degrees in the shade in the daytime, the air can't seem to cool off at night. John says a lot of people are sleeping out on their porches. We didn't build that kind of porch. Anyway, what we have we've used for storage.

**Friday, July 24, 1936**

Over 110 in the shade. There won't be many people here this weekend if it stays this hot. One of the men uptown proved you could fry an egg on the sidewalk. He did. The egg cooked.

---

[35]"Northeast Iowa Scenery Lauded by Motor Group, A.A.A. of Iowa Advises Trip to Decorah and Niagara Cave in News Release," *The Decorah Journal,* 17 Jun. 1936, p. 11, col. 3.

They're lucky to get an egg to try it with. Our few hens
don't lay in this kind of weather.

### Wednesday, September 2, 1936

Mary Dvorak dead? It doesn't seem possible. I thought
she would be here forever. Their big stone house where the
Soldiers Memorial stands was the saloon for many years.
They built the store that became for us Haug's Department
Store. Ah, Mary! You would talk to me any time any place.
And what a terrible time you had coming from Bohemia--
three months on the high seas. We didn't have any trouble at
all compared to that. Mary was about my age when she came
in 1854 and we came nine years later, better ships. But it still
wasn't easy.

### Thursday, September 10, 1936

My seventy-ninth birthday. Joe's fifty-sixth earlier this
week. I won't be like Anna and say I'll never be eighty. I'll
be proud to reach eighty if the Good Lord sees fit.

They talk a lot about Boulder Dam. The pictures make it
look like the eighth wonder of the world. It should really be
Hoover Dam, after our Iowa president who started it.

### Sunday, December 27, 1936

John wanted to go to Mass for his birthday, so we all went.

The boys worked all afternoon planning what I call the
Indian clock. Joe wants to call it "On the Lookout." It's the
Indians watching for the coming of the settlers.

### Thursday, January 21, 1937

We don't take these anniversaries for granted any more.
This is our fifty-eighth.

### Friday, April 16, 1937

Like it or not, Anna celebrated her fiftieth birthday. Joe
grinned and called her "The Golden Girl" for her "golden
anniversary." The boys have always loved to tease their little
sister. How she has brightened our family. We couldn't do
without her. She'll have to carry on when we are gone.

**Wednesday, June 23, 1937**

The boys went over to the neighbors last night where they had a radio hooked up to the car battery for the Joe Louis fight. Frank said they set the battery on the fender and the radio up on the hood.

**Sunday, July 4, 1937**

Joe and Frank brought a newspaper back from town. Everyone is talking about Amelia Earhart getting lost in the Pacific Ocean. Some say the Japanese captured her.

**Friday, September 10, 1937**

People are so nice to remember me on my eightieth. Even the ladies of the church sent out greetings and gifts.

**Monday, December 27, 1937**

John's birthday. The boys are carving the "On the Lookout Clock."

**January 1938**

Tonight I had onions frying in the pan along with liver when the boys brought the milk up from the barn. Frank said he could smell those onions halfway across the yard. If he ever starts a restaurant, he says he's going to have a fan blowing the smell of fried onions out onto the street. Everyone will simply be forced to follow their noses on inside.

**Friday, January 21, 1938**

Fifty-ninth anniversary. Who would have thought, when we stood together with John and Barbara Poshusta that we would be here in 1938! I wonder if we will live to our sixtieth. I don't even know what you call it. If silver is for twenty-five and gold for fifty, what symbolizes sixty? I shouldn't even think about that. We need to think about one day at a time and keeping each other well.

The boys keep well with their carving. In this cold weather they bring smaller things in to carve by our stove. That Indian looks into the far distance as if he can see to the end of the world. I suppose I should say, the end of his world, but that's what it turned out to be.

### Saturday, April 16, 1938

Anna at fifty-one seems adjusting to her age. She's sad at times, but then she misses having had a family of her own. When we are gone she will probably nurse her brothers in their old age. I don't see her as a nurse, however.

### Sunday, October 30, 1938

This may be the last time I'll write in this book. Frank tuned into a radio program that tells about the Martians landing in New Jersey. New Jersey lies a long way from here, but those monsters could be overhead at any moment. Joe and Frank went out and looked at the sky. They couldn't see anything. They were tuning in for Charlie McCarthy and got this news. It has been a good life. I am thankful to have lived so long. But what will happen to the young people?

### Monday, October 31, 1938

I guess the joke is on us. That radio program was just a made-up thing by some man called Orson Welles. I might as well confess to my diary as anywhere else that I fell for it.

### Saturday, January 21, 1939

Our sixtieth wedding anniversary!

### Sunday, April 16, 1939

Anna turned fifty-two and didn't say a thing about her age.

We weep for the Czecho-Slovakian Republic, destroyed this last month. When will the killing stop? Hitler has struck fear into the hearts of all of us.

*Mason City Globe Gazette*

BUICK MAGAZINE STORY IS ABOUT FAMED NORTH IOWANS: WORK OF BILY BROTHERS OF NORTHEAST IOWA IS NARRATED IN ARTICLE

In the current issue of the Buick magazine is an article concerning the famous Bily brothers of the Ridgeway vicinity and their clock-making activities. Writer of the story, "Time On Their Hands," is Jeannette Hegeman.

Miss Hegeman writes:

" . . . Motorists turn off the pavement between Decorah and Ridgeway, Iowa, to reach the Bily farm. An arrow with the word CLOCKS on it marks this place on No. 9. A three-mile drive on a winding, all-weather road brings them to the gateway, near which stands a small clock. There will probably be many cars headed in the same direction, as thousands of tourists file through the clockhouse nearly every month of the year. On No. 52, between Decorah and Calmar, there is a sign similar to the one near Ridgeway. It is a bit farther to the farm from this turn, but this road, too, is an all-weather one.

"On one side of the clockhouse, there are 18 large clocks of marvelous workmanship. These are the Bily hand-carved clocks . . . Joe and Frank Bily concentrated on clocks that told stories. . . .

"Chimes, organ-playing, gongs, and cuckooing tell the hours, half hours, and quarter hours in the clockhouse. All of the clocks are in running order, and the place is filled with a medley of sounds. A canary sings in the Clock of the Forest and a quail calls out 'Bob White' from the top of the tall mahogany hall clock."[36]

### Sunday, September 10, 1939

This morning, on my eighty-second birthday, I smell the scent of fall. I don't even know how I can celebrate and be happy when so many are dying in Europe. Charles Lindbergh has tried to keep us neutral, but how long can we stand aside? And should we be neutral if we can stop Hitler before it's too late?

### Sunday, October 1, 1939

Frank's birthday. Joe got him a carving tool. Maybe it will get Frank going again on carving.

### Thursday, December 27, 1939

John shows his age now at eighty-four. He says he should get the Vezinkas to give back his eyes.[37] That's a story he used to tell the children. Well, he can see, but not like he used to. We are all showing and feeling our age. The world is aflame and none of us is young enough to serve.

---

[36]"Buick Magazine Story is About Famed North Iowans, Work of Bily Brothers of Northeast Iowa Is Narrated in Article," *Mason City Globe-Gazette*, __ April 1939, n.p., n.c.

[37]"The Sun-Horse," a famous Bohemian fairy tale. Michael and Michael, pp. 1-13.

Johnny would have been sixty this December. He is as close to me as this writing pen. Of course, I think of him every day. Any two people who have spent as much time together as we did--no wonder.

# 8.
# WW II, Anna's Death, Clocks Moved to Spillville
## *1940-1949*

**Sunday, January 21, 1940**

Our sixty-first. We aren't good for much any more. Someone else needs to take up this book for me.

**Thursday, February 29, 1940**

It seems the world should not have an extra day if the peoples use it to fight. I once heard Father Bily give a homily on the text: "And the sun hasted not to go down for a day." The sunset delayed so that Joshua could finish his fighting and conquering of another people. This did not seem Christ-like to Father Bily and I have often thought of his daring to say it.

**Tuesday, April 16, 1940**
Anna spent a quiet fifty-third birthday here at home.

**Thursday, July 4, 1940**
The birthday of this great country means more to us this year than ever, when so many are imprisoned in Europe.

**Thursday, September 5, 1940**
We were so caught up in what has happened to the little countries we almost forgot it was Joe's sixtieth birthday. He asked, "Should I have lived so long to see what is happening in Poland, then Czechoslovakia? I have lived too long. Who does Hitler destroy next?"

**Tuesday, September 10, 1940**
I cry on my birthday, cry for those who have been run over in Europe.

**Tuesday, January 21, 1941**
Married sixty-two years. Each anniversary seems like it must surely be our last. But the Great Giver gives us more days.

**Wednesday, April 16, 1941**
Anna had to do all the "fixin's" for her Sunday birthday dinner. God bless Anna! What would we do without her? She remains the strong one who must carry on after we and the boys are gone.

**May 1941**
This morning I awakened with the first rooster's crowing and lay awhile enjoying the fragrance of the lilac blossoms. The lilacs certainly let you know when they come into bloom. Every bee and butterfly for miles around must know.

**Friday, July 4, 1941**
The news from Europe grows worse. We must do something. Lindbergh says we should stay out of it, but something must be done to stop Hitler.

**September 1941**
This morning the scent of fall hangs in the air.

**Friday, November 6, 1941**

Again the house echoes with its emptiness. My dear John has gone. We can expect to be called home--after all he was eighty-five--would have been eighty-six next month. I'm so glad I had him by my side all these years. Never a cross word did he utter.[38]

Father Chihak came out and gave him the Last Sacrament. We released him to Heaven.

When we opened the windows for Johnny, the smell of blossoms came in. Tonight it was the smell of snow.

**Sunday, December 7, 1941**

At noon the boys heard the news on the radio that the Japanese have attacked Pearl Harbor in Hawaii. President Roosevelt will speak to Congress tomorrow. John was spared from having to hear this. War comes quickly now.

**Thursday, December 25, 1941**

What a sad Christmas! So many young people are leaving home to go to war.

Christmas without any of the three Johns in my life--my father, Jan Andera whom I never got to know, my husband, and my son. The old song says it: "This world is not my home, I'm only passing through."

They're having blackouts on the coasts so enemy airplanes can't find targets. Maybe we shouldn't have our lights on, but Joe and Frank work in the long winter nights. They may have to stop that. They've been working on the "car clock," Joe calls it, planning it a couple of years. It's more than cars though--wagons, balloons, airplanes, trains. They will call it the "History of Travel Clock." The boys are so interested in the science magazines and cars and airplanes and zeppelins. Frank has been carving each kind of

---

[38]John Bily, died Friday, November 6, 1941, out at the farm. Joe dashed into town with the Model A Ford to get the young Father Chihak because they had no phone at the rectory. Father Chihak returned with Joe and gave John the comforting last rites of the Church, The Sacrament of Extreme Unction.

When John Bily expired, Father Chihak would recall that Mary, his wife, said, "Quick! Open the Window!" It was an old custom, to let the departing spirit fly away.

transportation and Joe has it figured out where each piece goes.

With the war on and the museum closed, no one may be able to see it. But, they feel like they have to keep working. It's their life.

### Wednesday, January 21, 1942

Our first anniversary apart. "'Til death we part," we promised and we kept it. I pray that he and Johnny are together. No one knows what it's like until it has happened. But we were old. I think of the young people dying in the war-- they had their lives ahead of them.

### Thursday, April 16, 1942

We couldn't get sugar for Anna's cake. How will we can fruits?

Her fifty-fifth. I remember how she used to talk about "no more birthdays." She has come to accept that Father Time marches on and we all grow older. The boys have even carved Father Time into two of their clocks.

The boys have stopped work on the "History of Travel Clock" and are helping the neighbors harvest. They can't stay out of farming entirely. They have decided to announce in the newspapers that there won't be any more clock tours during the war.

### August 1942

Yesterday the boys burned a patch of weeds. The bitter smell has gone all through the house. It's different than Frank's pipe. That has a mellow, almost soft-sour smell. But this weed burning makes my eyes water.

### Monday, September 5, 1942

Joe's sixty-second. Baked rice pudding. We have a ration card.

### Thursday, September 10, 1942

My eighty-fifth.

**Friday, December 25, 1942**

The boys have finished their "History of Travel" and are busy with the "Village Blacksmith." They learned that poem in school and always loved it.

**Monday, February 8, 1943**

The boys have been reading about how a transport ship was torpedoed off Greenland by a German submarine. The four chaplains on deck, a priest, a rabbi and two ministers, gave their life jackets to the sailors, then locked arms and prayed as they went down with the ship. Frank works himself up about it--doesn't even eat.

**Friday, April 16, 1943**

Anna's fifty-sixth birthday. She's my closest friend now. It was so different, with Johnny. I was his nurse. Now, probably, Anna will become my nurse. She would do everything for me if I would let her. Dear Anna, some young women give their lives to the church. You have given your life to us. You must have known we needed you.

**Sunday, December 19, 1943**

The impossible has happened. Anna left us last night from the Decorah Hospital. I had thought of everything that could happen, but this. An angel herself, she has joined the angels. Oh, why, oh why couldn't we have kept her longer? We thought surely she would outlast all of us. She had only been sick such a short time, then it turned into pneumonia. Even then, we were sure the hospital could do something for her. Doctors can do anything nowadays. But helping seemed beyond their power.

Now I'm worried about the boys. We are all so shocked and Frank talks out of his head--talks about burning the clocks. Nothing means anything, he said. Anna was the one who was to have the clocks and carry on. After all she had the idea of making the clocks a business, charging admission and all.

What will become of us? There will be no one left to carry on. I should turn my diary over to Frank.

**Tuesday, February 29, 1944**

A whole year without writing, dear diary. I am too old for this.

And the war goes on--another day when people fight and die. But, perhaps each day brings us closer to the end of Hitler. Perhaps I agree with Joshua's God after all.

**March 1944**

Today the sea gulls came up from the Gulf. They seem to know when the plowing starts. I remember how they would follow Joe and Frank all day when they turned over the fresh soil.

**November 1944**

The skies have been steel gray all day and the wind feels raw. The smell of snow drifts to me through the air. I can hardly hold my pen in hand.

**July 1945**

Mother asked me to pick up her diary where she has left off--a set of little books she has kept since her childhood.

Father Broz has retired. He has been cranky and tired for a long time. The war reaches toward the end. Hitler runs to his hole. Japan may fight us with everything they have, island by island, costing many lives for both sides.

Mother at eighty-eight has a right to retire from this diary. She has born the burdens for all of us, especially Johnny.

**August 1945**

Such an order of events! The dropping of a monstrous bomb, the surrender of Japan. We should all feel elated, but this will be different than the Armistice celebration of 1918. We know too much of war to release ourselves to joy. And, of course, the war does not end for those who have been maimed and have been in prison. We have exchanged our war for an age of a monster. I feel I should write quickly before we all burn.

**Wednesday, July 3, 1946**

Father Broz funeral yesterday. Thus ends an era in our lives. He buried our grandfather Matej in 1911, our brother

Johnny in 1932, our father only a month before Pearl Harbor, and our sister Anna in December of 1943.
This fall we move our clock business to Spillville.

*The Carmelite Review*
Napoleon Bonapart (was) responsible. If he had not decided to march on Russia in 1807 . . John Gaertner might never have been drafted [age 16]. [John's] Mother, a descendent of the family of the gentle St. Anthony of Padua. [promised to build a church if John returned.] John returned [safely]. Too poor to build a church.
Before John's mother died, she impressed on [him] the promise [to build a church if her son returned safely].
John journeyed to America. A French priest . . . spoke exultantly of beautiful country around Fort Atkinson.
John paddled down Ohio to Cairo, Illinois, up Mississippi to Dubuque, walked 100 miles to Fort Atkinson.
Back to Indiana [John brought] six families. Built a log cabin. First Mass for settlers. Cabin burned 1854. In 1885, when he was 90 years old, John was able to fulfill his mother's promise and [construct] the church on the location of the cabin where the first Mass was celebrated.[39]

### Sunday, February 29, 1948
Mother always noticed Leap Year and I should too. And she always remembered the death dates of our family. Anna died five years ago, almost at Christmas.

### Thursday, March 11, 1948
The Czechoslovakian Communists have said that Jan Masaryk has died from jumping from a window of the foreign ministry building. This sounds suspicious to me. Of course he may have been depressed after the Communist takeover, and that he tried to stay on and help. But he's not the kind of man to do what they say he did. At any rate the Communists can't use his good name. His father was the father of the Czech nation.

---

[39]Very Bradshaw, "The Smallest Church in the World," *The Carmelite Review*, 8, No. 8 (Feb. 1948), n.p., February, 1948.

**Tuesday, November 15, 1949**

Now, Mother left us. Only Joe and I remain. She lived more than a month past ninety-two.

We didn't take her to the hospital. She said that Anna went there and she didn't live through it. "When I die," she said, "I want to be at home."

We were planning to move in to Spillville. But she dreaded leaving the farm. Now she won't have to move. It's peculiar, the things one thinks about: Father died in November, Grandpa Matej died in November. I'll probably die in November. That spares one from enduring another winter.

**December 1949**

Moved in at last. Our home is on the creek, only a block or so from the clocks. Not much farther to walk than across the farmyard to the exhibit buildings.

# 9.

# End of an Era

## *1950-1965*

*Mason City Globe-Gazette*

THOUSANDS SEE FAMOUS BILY CLOCKS AT SPILLVILLE: ON DISPLAY IN DVORÁK HOME: WHITTLING PUT TO USE BY BROTHERS Spillville . . . Because two talented woodcarvers decided 40 years ago, to pursue their hobby, Spillville currently entertains 40,000 visitors a year. The Bily brothers now have completed more than 20 intricately carved timepieces, some standing 9 to 10 feet tall, with elaborate chimes and moving figures.

## VISIT DVORÁK HOME

Tourists who visit the Bily clocks also visit the scene of Spillville's earlier claim to cultural fame--the home of Doctor Antonin Dvorák. The clocks have been moved from the Bily farm home to the building in which Dvorák lived during the summer of 1893, while he made some final corrections on his *New World Symphony*, and composed several works for smaller groups.

Most of the clocks are displayed on the ground floor which in Dvorák's day was a tin shop. Upstairs, in the living rooms, curios and additional carvings are exhibited and there is an old organ. . . .

Joseph and Frank Bily, now 68 and 65, had been whittling since early childhood. . . . The Village Blacksmith

**107**

clock, inspired by Longfellow's poem, strikes the hour with the *Anvil Chorus* from *Il Trovatore*. It contains figures of the blacksmith, a farmer, his horse and dog, and all traditional blacksmith equipment.

A model of the Little Cathedral at nearby Festina has a tiny organ which plays *Lead Kindly Light* and other hymns.

. . . The Bily sense of humor is shown in at least one of the panels: It shows the one-room pioneer cabin, bulging with human and animal tenants, and is titled, "Always Room for One More."

. . . None of the Bily clocks has been sold. The town of Spillville will become owner of the collection eventually. The collection is to be kept intact, and to remain in the Dvorák building.

Admission to the building is 35 cents, which includes a tour and lecture.[40]

### Friday, February 29, 1952

Mother would have written on this day. She could have been an astronomer. I remember her standing out on the porch and looking at the stars. She always said one of those stars shone brighter after Johnny died.

### Tuesday, May 6, 1952

I do remember that this was the day that Johnny died, twenty years ago. Mother never got over it. Of course, she was close to him and met his every need. Joe and I, at least, gave him music every hour when the clocks went off. We did, until the clocks went out to the exhibit buildings. But, he occasionally heard them anyway when we wheeled him out to the shop. He'd sit there in the chair by the hour and watch us work. But when the big hands got near the top, he'd watch for the faces. It's funny the things one remembers after so many years.

*Mason City Globe-Gazette*

This year as in former years, it is expected that 40,000 people will visit Spillville (325 population) located along the Turkey River in Winneshiek County, 18 miles southeast of Cresco on State Highway 325. They are curious to see what

---

[40]"Thousands See Famous Bily Clocks at Spillville," *Mason City Globe-Gazette*, 19 Aug. 1951, n.p., n.c.

time it is. This remarkable interest in the time of day is because of the town's collection of hand-carved clocks which tell the hour in every possible way, and which includes the familiar cuckoo song to an intricate chimes version of Handel's *Largo*.[41]

**Wednesday, July 14, 1954**
So hot today--over 110 in the shade. It's hard on farm animals. In winter you can come in from the cold, but in summer there is no place to go. They say the asphalt they put on roads gets bubbles.

**Wednesday, February 29, 1956**
Leap Day.

**Monday, February 29, 1960**
Leap Day.

**Saturday, February 29, 1964**
Leap Day.

**Saturday, May 23, 1964**
My brother, my best friend, is dead. Somehow I don't feel the same grief I felt for Anna or my parents--just emptiness. Joe couldn't lift a pencil to sketch out a design. There was nothing left for him in this world.

I too am ready to go, "when He calls."

We opened the windows for Joseph's spirit to go, the way we did in May of 1932 for Johnny. Back then in 1932 we could smell the apple blossoms when we threw up the sashes. Now I can't smell anything.

**Friday, January 8, 1965**
I've left my home in Spillville. They said I could bring personal things--a chair, a clock. I brought this diary--a last request of my mother. But now I find it hard to write. I feel that the clocks are in good hands with the Anderas and Poshustas, and the town of Spillville.

---

[41]Earl Jay Widman, Jr., "Bily Brothers of Spillville Design a Variety of Clocks, *Mason City Globe-Gazette*, 14 Jul. 1955, n.p., n.c.

**March 1965**

Saint Wenceslaus changes. The altar that we knew is gone. The stations of the cross have gone to African missions. The priest faces us. Perhaps this should be.

Younger hands must take over. I would go down like the chaplains on board the ship--their life preservers in the hands of the young folks who have their lives ahead of them.

**April 1965**

I thought I could smell the apple blossoms.

**Sunday, September 5, 1965**

Joe's birthday. My second year without him.

**Sunday, October 31, 1965**

All Saints Day tomorrow. All my family has gone to heaven. Now comes the time of year when Bilys die. We get ready for the long winter and, then, depart.[42]

---

[42]Frank Bily died November 25, 1965, in the Decorah Retirement Center. "Frank Bily, Famed Clock Maker, Dies at Age 81," *Mason City Globe-Gazette*, 26 Nov. 1965, n.p., n.c.

GREATNESS
A man is as great as the dreams he dreams,
As great as the love he bears
As great as the values he deems,
The happiness he shares.

A man is as great as the thoughts he thinks,
As the worth he has attained,
As the fountains at which his spirit drinks,
And the insight he has gained.

A man is as great as the truth he speaks,
As great as the help he gives,
As great as the destiny he seeks,
As great as the life he lives.

                    -Charles Edwin Flynn[43]

*Frank and his brother Joe are known by the company they kept, the heroes they admired. They gave their lives, to the celebration of greatness--the heroes they admired.*

---

[43]A favorite poem of Dr. R. M. "Doc" Good, president 1921-1952, School of the Ozarks. Charles Edwin Flynn, "Greatness," *College of the Ozarks Alumni News*, vol. 58, no. 2, Fall 1992, p. 7.

# Select Bibliography

**BOOKS**

Beall, Blanche M. *The Bily Clocks.* 12th printing n.p.: West Union Argo-Gazette, 1932.

Baily, Edwin C. *Past and Present of Winneshiek County, Iowa: A Record of Settlement, Organization, Progress and Achievement.* Chicago: S.J. Clarke Publishing Company, 1913, Vol. I.

*The Bily Clocks of Spillville, Iowa* [United States]: n.p., n.d.

Emmott, Elizabeth Braithwaite. *The Story of Quakerism.* London: Headley Brothers, 1912.

Klimesh, Cyril M. *They Came to This Place, A History of Spillville, Iowa and Its Czech Settlers.* Sebastopol, CA: Methodius Press, 1983.

Michael, Maurice and Pamela Michael. *Fairy Tales from Bohemia,* Chicago: Follett Publishing Company, 1966.

Neuzil, Becky and Beatrice Sbiral, eds. *The Quasquicentennial History Book, 1860-1985, Spillville, Iowa.* Spillville, IA: n.p., 1985.

Trnka, Nina. *Czech-English, English-Czech Dictionary.* New York: Hippocrene, rev. ed. 1991.

## PAMPHLETS

Bily Clock Exhibit. *The Bily Clocks Tour.* Spillville, Iowa:
Bily Clock Exhibit, n.d.
Bily Clock Exhibit. *Visit Spillville Home of Antonin Dvořák
and the Bily Clocks.* Spillville, Iowa: Bily Clock Exhibit,
n.d.
*History of Spillville.* Spillville, Iowa: n.p., n.d.
Reidle Products. *Fretwork Patterns & Supplies, Catalog 104.*
1992.
*Short History of the Bily Brothers.* Spillville, Iowa, n.p., n.d.
Wild, H. L. *Wild's Latest Designs and Price List of Scroll
Sawyers Materials.* New York, New York: H. L. Wild,
Publisher, n.d.


## NEWSPAPERS

"21,000 See Bily Clocks In New Home." *The Dubuque
Telegraph Herald,* n.d. 1946, n.p., n.c.
Anderson, Phil Lamar. "Throngs Attracted to Clock
Collection of Bily Brothers on Ridgeway Farm." *Mason
City Globe-Gazette,* 11 Jun. 1931, n.p., n.c.
"Anna Bily Dead; Buried Tuesday." *The Decorah Public
Opinion,* 22 Dec. 1943, p. 4, n.c.
"Bily Brother Dies at Spillville, Carved Famous Clocks."
*The Waterloo Courier,* 26 Nov. 1965, p. 10, n.c.
"Bily Brothers' Clocks at Spillville Expected to Attract 40,000
Tourists." [Dubuque, IA] *The Telegraph Herald,* 2 Sept.
1954, p. 26, n.c.
"'Bily Clocks' in Films Here." *The Decorah Journal,* 5 Aug.
1936, p. 1, col. 2.
"Brothers Carve Unusual Clock." *Mason City Globe-Gazette,*
28 May 1928, n.p., n.c.
"Buick Magazine Story Is About Famed North Iowans, Work
of Bily Brothers of Northeast Iowa Is Narrated in Article."
*Mason City Globe-Gazette,* __ April 1939, n.p., n.c.
Clark, Florence L. "First of Hordes of Season's Tourists
Visit Spillville's Bily Clock Collection." [Dubuque, IA]
*The Telegraph Herald,* 24 Jun. 1955, n.p., n.c.
"Clock Maker Bily Is Dead." *Mason City Globe-Gazette,* __
Nov. 1965.

"Clocks May Be Shown at Chicago." *The Decorah Public Opinion*, 4 Sept. 1930, Sec. B, p.1, c. 2.

"Decorah Gives Fine Publicity." *The Decorah Journal*, 6 May 1936, p. 6, cols. 7-8.

"Frank Bily, Famed Clock Maker, Dies at Age 81." *Mason City Globe-Gazette*, 26 Nov. 1965, n.p., n.c.

"'Grandma' Mary Dvorak, Spillville's Oldest Resident, Died Last Tuesday." *The Decorah Journal*, 2 Sept. 1936, p. 1, cols. 6-7.

"John Bily, 52, Dies on Spillville Farm, Was Brother of Frank and Joseph, Makers of World Famous Clocks." *The Decorah Journal*, 11 May 1932, p. 6, n.c.

Juve, Don. "Spillville's Famed Exhibit Is Open Daily." [Dubuque, IA] *The Telegraph Herald*, n.d., n.p., n.c.

Lucas, Ray. "Ray Lucas Writes a Wholesome Essay on the Majesty of Trees." *The Decorah Journal*, 2 Sept. 1931, n.p., n.c.

"Mrs. Mary Bily Died Monday at Spillville." *The Decorah Public Opinion*, 17 Nov. 1949, p. 1, n.c.

Musser, Gerry. "West Union Craftsman Heals Wounds of Time." *Mason City Globe-Gazette*, n.d., Sec. A, n.p.

"Northeast Iowa Scenery Lauded by Motor Group, A.A.A. of Iowa Advises Trip to Decorah and Niagara Cave in News Release." *The Decorah Journal*, 17 Jun. 1936, p. 11, col. 3.

"Organize to Help Bohemia, People of Spillville Take on New War Work, Will Aid Czechs to Obtain Their Liberty and Take Their Right Place in the World." *The Decorah Republican*, 22 Aug. 1918, n.p., n.c.

"Paradise Clock Made." *Mason City Globe-Gazette*, 26 Jul. 1936, n.p., n.c.

"Pictures of Decorah Sought by Conoco's Travel Bureau Again." *The Decorah Journal*, 15 Jan. 1936, p. 6, col. 4.

Sanderson, Veryl. "Repair Problem Foreseen for Famed Bily Clocks." *The Waterloo Courier*, 14 Aug. 1966, p. 18, n.c.

"Scenic Beauties of Decorah and Winneshiek County Told to East by Mrs. Biermann in Radio Talk." *The Decorah Journal*, 11 Mar. 1936, p. 4, cols. 3-4.

"See the World's Fair for Fifteen Cents." *The Ridgeway Recorder*, 18 Jul. 1893, n.p., n.c.

"Services Today for Frank Bily, Clock Maker Died
  Thursday in Hospital." *The Decorah Public Opinion*, 29
  Nov. 1965, pp. 1-5, n.c.
"Shaping of Wood Played Important Spillville Role." *The
  Waterloo Courier*, 14 Feb. 1965, p. 19, n.c.
Sharpe, R. Lee. "Old Time Editor Decides to Write True
  Wedding Story." *The Decorah Journal*, 26 Aug. 1931,
  n.p., n.c.
"Spillville, Death of a Pioneer." *The Decorah Public
  Opinion*, 11 Nov. 1941, n.p., n.c.
"Thousands See Famous Bily Clocks at Spillville." *Mason
  City Globe-Gazette*, 19 Sept. 1951, n.p., n.c.
[title not available]. *The St. Paul Pioneer Press*, 16 Jun. 1929,
  n.p., n.c.
Walk, Chuck. "History Attracts Tourists." *Mason City
  Globe-Gazette*, Summer 1960, n.p., n.c.
"Wednesday Rites for Joe Bily." *Mason City Globe-Gazette*,
  25 May 1964, n.p., n.c.
Widman ,Jr., Earl Jay. "Bily Brothers of Spillville Design a
  Variety of Clocks." *Mason City Globe-Gazette*, 14 Jul.
  1955, n.p., n.c.
"Winneshiek County Boys Make Clocks for Pastime."
  *Decorah Republican*, n.d., n.p., n.c.


## PERIODICALS

Flynn, Charles Edwin. "Greatness." *College of the Ozarks
  Alumni News*, 58, no. 2, Fall 1992, p. 7.
Klimesh, Cyril M. "Charles Andera, Czech Pioneer." *"Nase
  Dejiny" The Magazine of Czech Genealogy and Culture*,
  VIII, No. 4 (1988), pp. 8-11.
"Time Marches On." *Yester News*, xv, No. 9 (1963), pp. 1-5.


## PERSONAL LETTERS

Andera, Robert. Letter to Duane Hutchinson. 21 Jul. 1989.
  Author's collection.
Bily Brothers. Letter to James Reidle. 30 Jun. 1953. James
  Reidle collection.

Bina, Srs. M. Raphael and M. Antonia Bina. Letter to Duane Hutchinson. 15 Jul. 1990. Author's collection.

Fenstermann, Duane W. Letter to Rosemary Palmer, Consulting Corporate Archivest, Cargill, Inc. 19 April 1991. Author's collection.

Hutchinson, Duane. Letter to Robert Andera, Robert Balik, Vernon Brekke, Cyril M. Klimesh, Rusty Poshusta. 2 Sept. 1992.

Poshusta, Rusty. Letter to author. n.d. 1993.

Klimesh, Cyril M. Letter to Duane Hutchinson. 16 Jul. 1990. Author's collection.

_____. Letter to Duane Hutchinson. 28 Jul. 1990. Author's collection.

_____. Letter to Duane Hutchinson. 12 Sept. 1992. Author's collection.

_____. Letter to Duane Hutchinson. 26 Apr. 1993. Author's collection.

**INDIRECT SOURCES**

Lowenbach, Dr. Jan. *Joseph Jan Kovarik, Dvorák's American Secretary*, n.p., n.d.

# Index of Names 119